It's another great book from CGP...

Maths exams can seem daunting — especially if you're not sure what to expect.
But they're less stressful if you've done plenty of realistic practice in advance.

Happily, this book (which includes a **free** Online Edition)
is packed with exam-style questions to fully prepare you for the real thing.
We've even thrown in practice exams with online video solutions.

How to get your free online extras

Want to read this book on your computer or tablet?
Just go to **cgpbooks.co.uk/extras** and enter this code...

0760 8777 2340 0618

By the way, this code only works for one person. If somebody else has used
this book before you, they might have already claimed the online extras.

CGP — still the best! ☺

Our sole aim here at CGP is to produce the highest quality books —
carefully written, immaculately presented and dangerously close to being funny.

Then we work our socks off to get them out to you
— at the cheapest possible prices.

Contents

☑ Use the tick boxes to check off the topics you've completed.

Section Five — Angles and Geometry

Section Six — Measures

Section Seven — Statistics and Probability

Practice Papers

Published by CGP

Editors:
Katherine Craig, Ceara Hayden, Kirstie McHale, Sarah Oxley, Sam Pilgrim,
David Ryan, Megan Tyler, Rachel Ward.

Contributors:
Andrew Ballard, Terence Brown, Pamela Chatley, Claire Jackson, Rosie Hanson.

With thanks to Alastair Duncombe, Mark Moody and Glenn Rogers for the proofreading.

ISBN: 978 1 84762 978 4

Clipart from Corel®
Printed by Elanders Ltd, Newcastle upon Tyne

Based on the classic CGP style created by Richard Parsons.

How to Use This Book

- Hold the book <u>upright</u>, approximately <u>50 cm</u> from your face, ensuring that the text looks like <u>this</u>, not ⁻ᵗʰⁱˢ. Alternatively, place the book on a <u>horizontal</u> surface (e.g. a table or desk) and sit adjacent to the book, at a distance which doesn't make the text too small to read.

- In case of emergency, press the two halves of the book together <u>firmly</u> in order to close.

- Before attempting to use this book, familiarise yourself with the following <u>safety information</u>:

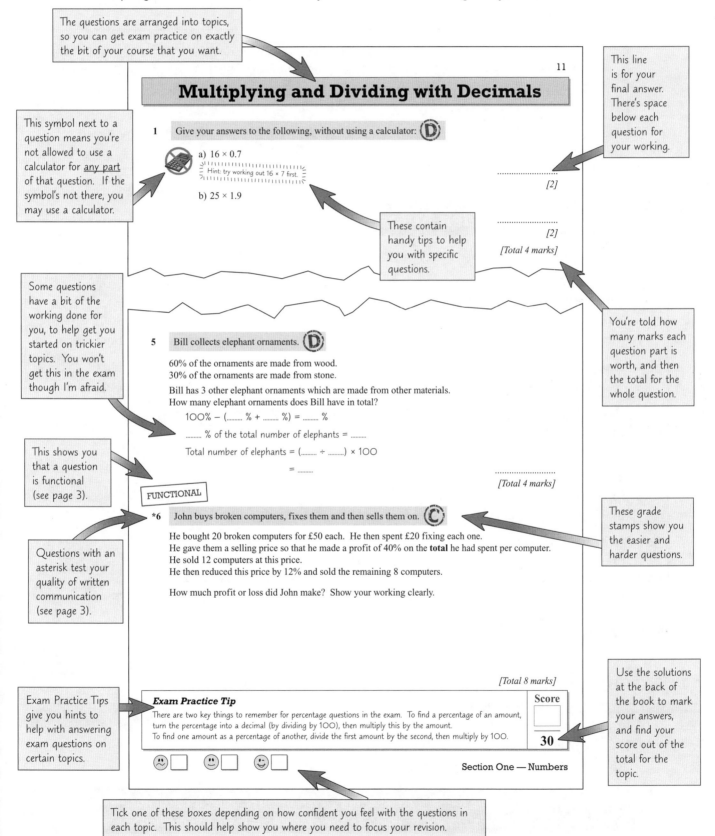

The questions are arranged into topics, so you can get exam practice on exactly the bit of your course that you want.

This line is for your final answer. There's space below each question for your working.

This symbol next to a question means you're not allowed to use a calculator for <u>any part</u> of that question. If the symbol's not there, you may use a calculator.

These contain handy tips to help you with specific questions.

Some questions have a bit of the working done for you, to help get you started on trickier topics. You won't get this in the exam though I'm afraid.

This shows you that a question is functional (see page 3).

Questions with an asterisk test your quality of written communication (see page 3).

You're told how many marks each question part is worth, and then the total for the whole question.

These grade stamps show you the easier and harder questions.

Use the solutions at the back of the book to mark your answers, and find your score out of the total for the topic.

Exam Practice Tips give you hints to help with answering exam questions on certain topics.

11

Multiplying and Dividing with Decimals

1   Give your answers to the following, without using a calculator: **D**

a) 16 × 0.7

Hint: try working out 16 × 7 first.

b) 25 × 1.9

.... [2]

.... [2]
[Total 4 marks]

5   Bill collects elephant ornaments. **D**

60% of the ornaments are made from wood.
30% of the ornaments are made from stone.

Bill has 3 other elephant ornaments which are made from other materials.
How many elephant ornaments does Bill have in total?

100% − (......... % + ... %) = ... %

.... % of the total number of elephants = ...

Total number of elephants = (......... ÷ ....) × 100

= ....

.... [Total 4 marks]

FUNCTIONAL

*6   John buys broken computers, fixes them and then sells them on. **C**

He bought 20 broken computers for £50 each. He then spent £20 fixing each one.
He gave them a selling price so that he made a profit of 40% on the **total** he had spent per computer.
He sold 12 computers at this price.
He then reduced this price by 12% and sold the remaining 8 computers.

How much profit or loss did John make? Show your working clearly.

[Total 8 marks]

Exam Practice Tip
There are two key things to remember for percentage questions in the exam. To find a percentage of an amount, turn the percentage into a decimal (by dividing by 100), then multiply this by the amount.
To find one amount as a percentage of another, divide the first amount by the second, then multiply by 100.

☹ ☐   😐 ☐   🙂 ☐

Score

30

Section One — Numbers

Tick one of these boxes depending on how confident you feel with the questions in each topic. This should help show you where you need to focus your revision.

Exam Tips

Edexcel Exam Stuff

1) If you're studying the Edexcel linear course (Mathematics A) you will have <u>two</u> exams — one <u>calculator</u> exam and one <u>non-calculator</u> exam.

If you're studying the Mathematics B course, you'll have <u>three</u> exams — <u>one</u> of which is a non-calculator paper.

2) Both exams are <u>1hr 45mins</u> long and both are worth <u>100 marks</u>.

3) Timings in the exam are really important, so here's a quick guide...

- As each paper is worth <u>100 marks</u> and you've got <u>105 minutes</u> to complete the paper, you should spend about a <u>minute per mark</u> working on each question (i.e. 2 marks = 2 mins).

- That'll leave you with <u>5 minutes</u> at the end of the exam to <u>check</u> back through your answers and make sure you haven't made any silly mistakes. <u>Not</u> to just stare at that hottie in front.

- If you're totally, hopelessly stuck on a question, just <u>leave it</u> and <u>move on</u> to the next one. You can always <u>go back</u> to it at the end if you've got enough time.

There are a Few Golden Rules

1) **Always, always, always make sure you <u>read the question properly</u>.**
   For example, if the question asks you to give your answer in metres, <u>don't</u> give it in centimetres.

2) **Show <u>each step</u> in your <u>working</u>.**
   You're less likely to make a mistake if you write things out in stages. And even if your final answer's wrong, you'll probably pick up <u>some marks</u> if the examiner can see that your <u>method</u> is right.

3) **Check that your answer is <u>sensible</u>.**
   Worked out an angle of 450° or 0.045° in a triangle? You've probably gone wrong somewhere...

4) **Make sure you give your answer to the right <u>degree of accuracy</u>.**
   The question might ask you to round to a certain number of <u>significant figures</u> or <u>decimal places</u>. So make sure you do just that, otherwise you'll almost certainly lose marks.

5) **Look at the number of <u>marks</u> a question is worth.**
   If a question's worth 2 or more marks, you're not going to get them all for just writing down the final answer — you're going to have to <u>show your working</u>.

6) **Write your answers as <u>clearly</u> as you can.**
   If the examiner can't read your answer you won't get any marks, even if it's right.

Obeying these Golden Rules will help you get as many marks as you can in the exam — but they're no use if you haven't learnt the stuff in the first place. So make sure you revise well and do <u>as many</u> practice questions as you can.

Using Your Calculator

1) Your calculator can make questions a lot easier for you, but only if you <u>know how to use it</u>. Make sure you know what the different buttons do and how to use them.

2) If you're working out a <u>big calculation</u> on your calculator, it's best to do it in <u>stages</u> and use the <u>memory</u> to store the answers to the different parts. If you try and do it all in one go, it's too easy to mess it up.

3) If you're feeling reckless, and decide to do a question all in one go on your calculator, use <u>brackets</u> so the calculator knows which bits to do first.

REMEMBER: <u>Golden Rule number 2</u> still applies, even if you're using a calculator — you should still write down <u>all</u> the steps you're doing so the examiner can see the method you're using.

You Need to Understand the Command Words

<u>Command words</u> are the words in a question that tell you <u>what to do</u>.
If you don't know what they mean, you might not be able to answer the questions properly.

Calculate...   This means you'll have to <u>work something out</u> — either using pen and paper OR your calculator.

Work out...   This is a bit like 'calculate', except you might be able to do the sum in your head.

Find...   You'll have to use a mixture of <u>problem-solving</u> skills and maths to find the answer to a question. It might not be immediately obvious what calculation you have to do.

Explain...   You have to use words to <u>give reasons</u> for something.

Show that...   You have to <u>use maths</u> to show that something is true.

> With 'explain' and 'show that' questions, the number of marks available can give you an idea of how much you need to write.

Functional Questions

> On Foundation Tier papers, 30-40% of the total marks available are from functional questions.

Some of the questions in your exams will be <u>wordy</u> questions about a <u>real-life situation</u>.

These are called functional questions. Functional questions are a bit trickier than normal questions because you have to <u>work out</u> what you are <u>being asked to do</u>. Here are some <u>useful steps</u> to follow:

1) <u>Read the question</u> carefully so you can work out <u>what maths you need</u> to use.

2) <u>Underline</u> the information that you <u>need</u> to <u>answer the question</u>
— you won't always have to use all of the numbers they give you.

3) <u>Write</u> the question out in <u>maths</u> and then answer it, <u>showing your working</u> as usual.

In this book, questions which contain functional elements are marked with this stamp: FUNCTIONAL

Your exam paper <u>won't</u> mark them up though, so try to get used to how these questions look, so that you can spot them in your exam.

Quality of Written Communication

> This may seem daft when it's a maths exam, but if the examiner doesn't think you've communicated your answer well enough, you'll lose marks.

In the exam, questions that have an <u>asterisk</u> (*) next to them are questions which test your <u>quality of written communication</u>. This means you'll be tested on your ability to explain things clearly, as well as your ability to do good maths. When you're answering questions like this, make sure you...

• Use your neatest <u>handwriting</u> so the examiner can easily read your answer.

• Check that your <u>spelling</u>, <u>punctuation</u> and <u>grammar</u> are ~~rigit rihgt~~ correct.

• Show <u>every step</u> of your working, and lay it out in a <u>clear</u> and <u>coherent</u> way.

• Use <u>specialist wording</u> if you need to.

(You should already be doing all these things in every answer anyway, so they're really nothing to worry about...)

Ordering Numbers and Place Value

1 Use the number lines to answer the following questions.

a) Write down the number shown by the arrow below. (G)

50   ↑   60   70

....

[1]

b) Write down the number shown by the arrow below. (G)

400   500   ↑   600   700

....

[1]

c) Find 2.6 on the number line below and mark it with an arrow (↑). (F)

2   3   4

[1]

[Total 3 marks]

2 Answer each of the following. (G)

a) Write 5079 in words.

....

[1]

b) Write six thousand, one hundred and five as a number.

....

[1]

c) What is the value of the figure 9 in 13 692?

....

[1]

[Total 3 marks]

3 Answer these questions. (G)

a) Write 26 004 in words.

....

[1]

b) Write twenty thousand, three hundred and sixty-four as a number.

....

[1]

c) What is the value of the figure 8 in 65 803?

....

[1]

[Total 3 marks]

4 Answer the following questions. (G)

a) Write 420 457 in words.

....
[1]

b) Write six million as a number.

....
[1]

c) Write down the value of the figure 2 in 102 487

....
[1]

[Total 3 marks]

---

5 The mileages of four cars are given below. Put the distances in order, starting with the lowest. (F)

98 653   100 003   98 649   100 010

.... , ... , ... , ...
[Total 1 mark]

---

6 Put these numbers in order of size, from high to low. (F)

53.3   35.6   35.54   52.91   35.06

.... , ... , ... , ... , ...
[Total 1 mark]

---

7 Anne has five cards, each with a number written on. (G)

4   7   1   8   2

She lines up all the cards to make a 5 digit number.

a) What is the smallest number she can make?

....
[1]

b) What is the largest number she can make?

....
[1]

[Total 2 marks]

Score:

16

Addition and Subtraction

1 Jamie has 522 stickers. He gives 197 to his brother and 24 to his sister. **(G)**
How many stickers does he have left?

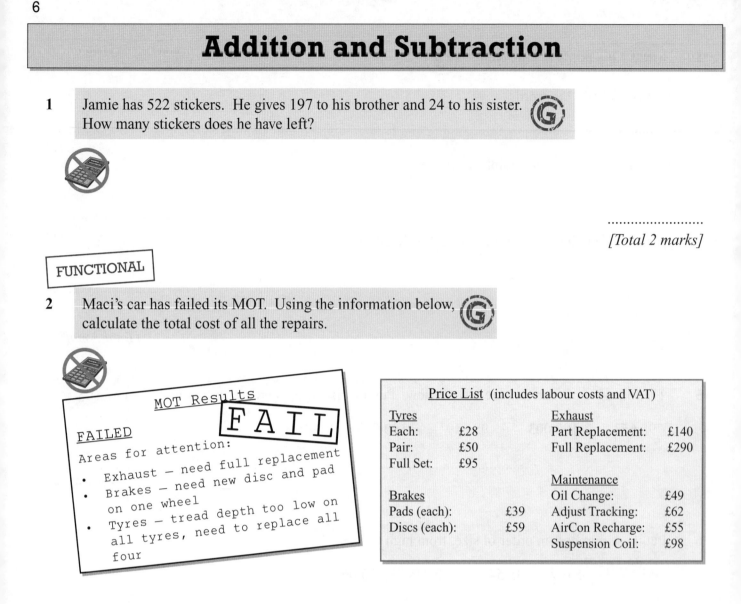

....
[Total 2 marks]

FUNCTIONAL

2 Maci's car has failed its MOT. Using the information below, **(G)**
calculate the total cost of all the repairs.

MOT Results

FAIL

FAILED

Areas for attention:

- Exhaust — need full replacement
- Brakes — need new disc and pad on one wheel
- Tyres — tread depth too low on all tyres, need to replace all four

Price List (includes labour costs and VAT)		
Tyres		**Exhaust**
Each: £28		Part Replacement: £140
Pair: £50		Full Replacement: £290
Full Set: £95		
		Maintenance
Brakes		Oil Change: £49
Pads (each):	£39	Adjust Tracking: £62
Discs (each):	£59	AirCon Recharge: £55
		Suspension Coil: £98

£ ....
[Total 3 marks]

3 Eric goes to town with £15. He spends £8.50 on a new scarf. **(F)**
He meets his nan who gives him £20 and tells him to take £10 of it home for his sister.
Eric then sees a jumper he likes which costs £18.

 If Eric buys the jumper, will he still have £10 to give to his sister?
Show how you worked out your answer.

[Total 2 marks]

4 Sue and Alan meet Mark in a juice bar.
Mark offers to buy a round of drinks.

 Mark wants a Passion Fruit Punch and
Sue and Alan both want a Tutti Frutti.

Mark pays with a £10 note.
How much change will he get?

Juice Bar Price List	
St Clements:	£2.80
Cranberry Crush:	£2.90
Tutti Frutti:	£2.40
Passion Fruit Punch:	£2.15

£ ....

[Total 2 marks]

5 Parvati and Zayn stop at a café for breakfast. (F)

New Road Café

Breakfast Snacks:		*Drinks:*	
Toast (2 slices)	£1.50	Tea	£1.40
Yoghurt with fruit	£1.90	Coffee	£1.50
Raisin bagel	£2.30	Fresh orange juice	£1.80

Breakfast deal of the day:
Raisin bagel & fresh orange juice £3.40

Parvati has £3.30 and wants a breakfast snack and a hot drink.

a) List two combinations of snack and hot drink that she can get.

....

[2]

Zayn buys 2 raisin bagels, a tea, a coffee and a fresh orange juice.
He pays the lowest possible price.

b) If he pays with a £10 note, how much change will he get?

Hint: don't forget the deal of the day.

£ ....

[3]

[Total 5 marks]

Score:

14

Section One — Numbers

Multiplying and Dividing by 10, 100, etc.

1 Work out:

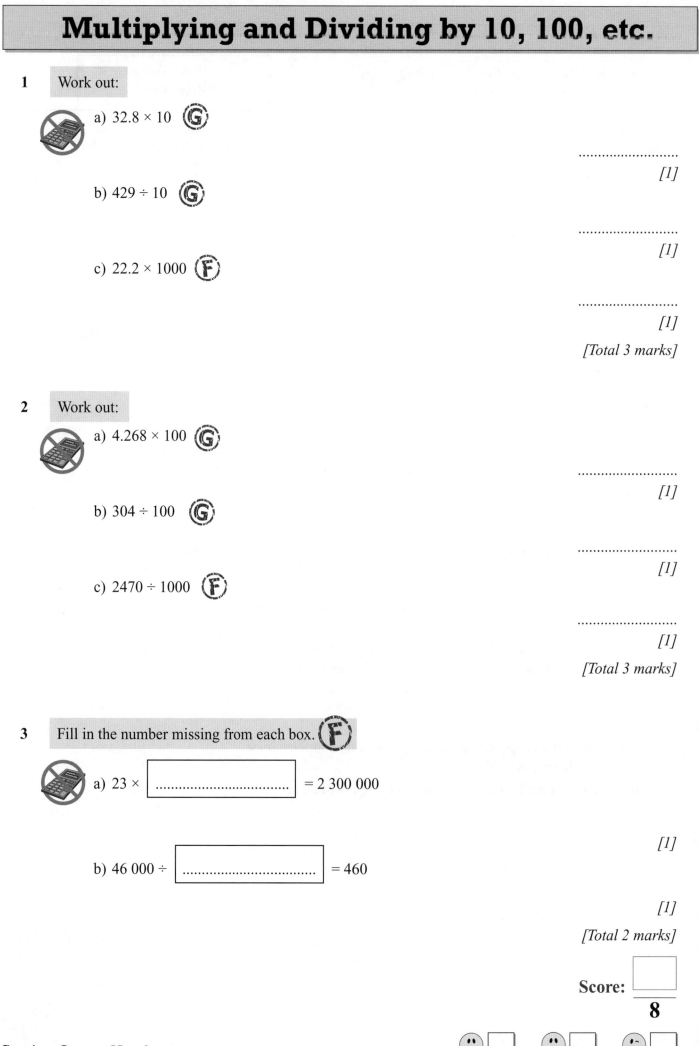

a) 32.8 × 10 **G**

....

[1]

b) 429 ÷ 10 **G**

....

[1]

c) 22.2 × 1000 **F**

....

[1]

[Total 3 marks]

2 Work out:

a) 4.268 × 100 **G**

....

[1]

b) 304 ÷ 100 **G**

....

[1]

c) 2470 ÷ 1000 **F**

....

[1]

[Total 3 marks]

3 Fill in the number missing from each box. **F**

a) 23 × [........................] = 2 300 000

[1]

b) 46 000 ÷ [........................] = 460

[1]

[Total 2 marks]

Score: [   ]

8

Multiplying and Dividing Without a Calculator

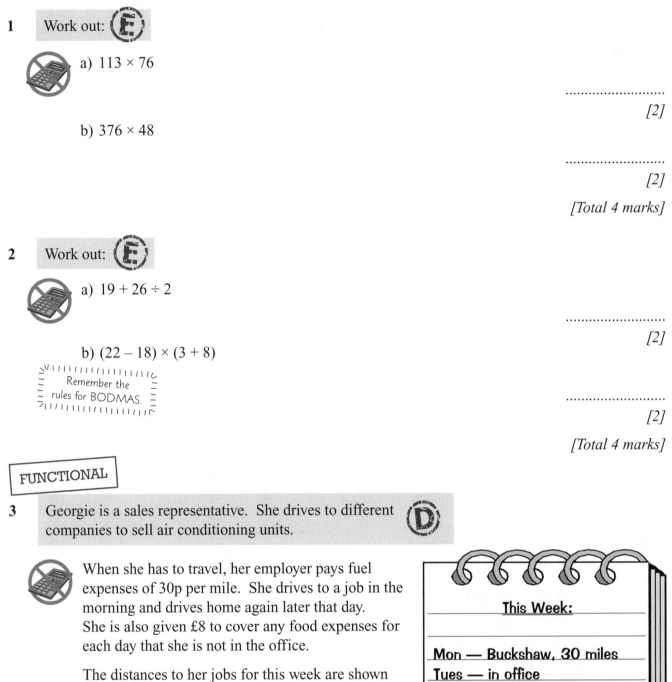

1 Work out: **E**

a) 113 × 76

....
[2]

b) 376 × 48

....
[2]

[Total 4 marks]

2 Work out: **E**

a) 19 + 26 ÷ 2

....
[2]

b) (22 − 18) × (3 + 8)

Remember the rules for BODMAS.

....
[2]

[Total 4 marks]

FUNCTIONAL

3 Georgie is a sales representative. She drives to different companies to sell air conditioning units. **D**

When she has to travel, her employer pays fuel expenses of 30p per mile. She drives to a job in the morning and drives home again later that day. She is also given £8 to cover any food expenses for each day that she is not in the office.

The distances to her jobs for this week are shown on the right.

Find Georgie's total expenses for this week.

Hint: think carefully about the total distance travelled.

This Week:

Mon — Buckshaw, 30 miles
Tues — in office
Weds — Wortham, 28 miles
Thurs — Harborough, 39 miles
Fri — Scotby, 40 miles

£ ....
[Total 5 marks]

Section One — Numbers

4   Paul is making cushions with braid around the edges.
He has 756 inches of braid. He needs 54 inches for each cushion.

How many cushions does he have enough braid for?

....

[Total 2 marks]

5   Alanna buys 15 tickets for a concert for her and some friends.
Each ticket is the same price. She pays with £200 and gets £5 change.

How much does each ticket cost?

£ ....

[Total 3 marks]

FUNCTIONAL

6   James is having a party. He has worked out how much food he needs
to buy per person and goes to the shop to buy the things that he needs.

Crisps come in 300 g packets.

There are 8 slices per pizza.

James is expecting there to be 15 people,
including himself, at the party.

> For each person:
> * 3 slices of pizza
> * 25 g of crisps

How many pizzas and how many packets of crisps does he need to buy?

.... pizzas

.... packets of crisps

[Total 5 marks]

Exam Practice Tip

It's always important to show your working, but it's especially important for these non-calculator questions — because they all include marks for using a correct method. If you don't show your working, you'll be throwing away valuable marks in the exam.

Score

23

Multiplying and Dividing with Decimals

1   Give your answers to the following, without using a calculator:

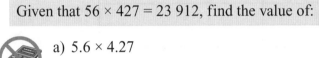
     a) 16×0.7

Hint: try working out 16×7 first.

     b) 25×1.9

....
[2]

....
[2]

[Total 4 marks]

2   Given that $56 \times 427 = 23\,912$, find the value of: (D)

     a) 5.6×4.27

....
[1]

     b) $0.56 \times 4\,270\,000$

....
[1]

     c) $2391.2 \div 4.27$

....
[1]

[Total 3 marks]

3   Work out 0.7×0.8 (D)

....
[Total 2 marks]

4   Work out the value of each of the following: (D)

     a) $14 \div 0.7$

$$14 \div 0.7 = \frac{14}{0.7} = \frac{\ldots\ldots}{7} = \ldots\ldots$$

....
[2]

     b) $23 \div 0.46$

....
[2]

[Total 4 marks]

Score:

13

Negative Numbers

1 Put the numbers below in order from lowest to highest. (F)

−102.4   98.9   −102.7   99.5   −99.8   −98.9   −103.1

.... , ... , ... , ... , ... , ... , ...

[Total 1 mark]

2 The table below shows the minimum and maximum (F) temperatures in four cities one day in January.

City	Min. temperature (°C)	Max. temperature (°C)
London	4	9
Paris	7	11
St Petersburg	−8	−2
Christchurch	16	22

a) What was the difference between the maximum and minimum temperatures in London?

.... °C

[1]

b) Which city had the **lowest** minimum temperature?

....

[1]

c) What was the difference in temperature between the highest maximum temperature and the lowest minimum temperature across the four cities?

.... °C

[3]

[Total 5 marks]

3 Work out: (E)

a) −11 × 7

....

[1]

b) −72 ÷ −8

....

[1]

[Total 2 marks]

Score:

8

Special Types of Number

1   Choose a number from the list which matches each description.

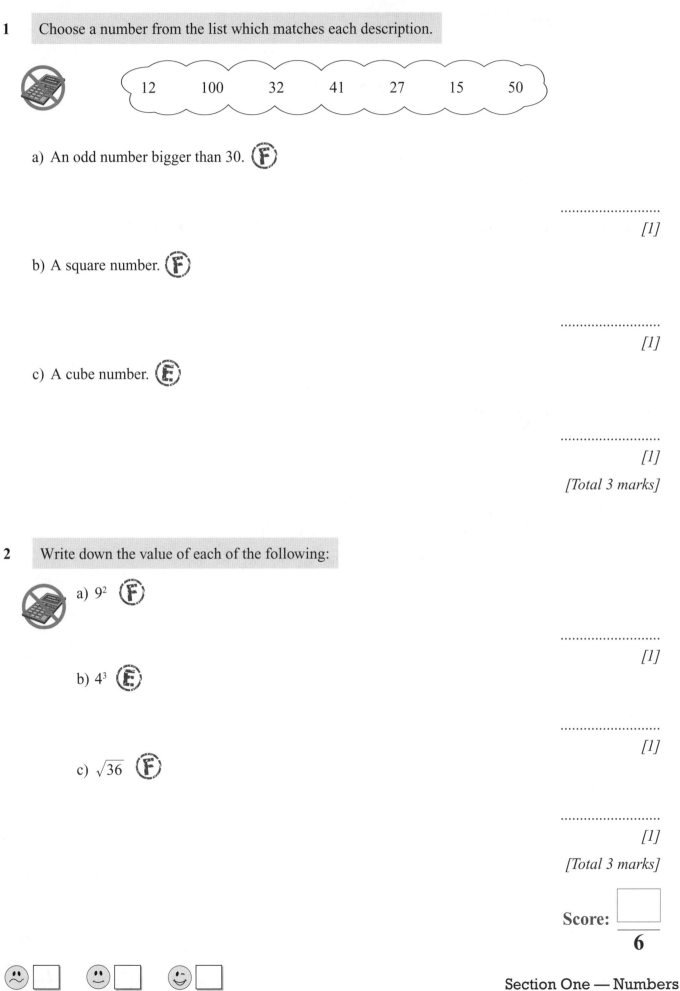

12   100   32   41   27   15   50

a) An odd number bigger than 30. (F)

....
[1]

b) A square number. (F)

....
[1]

c) A cube number. (E)

....
[1]

[Total 3 marks]

2   Write down the value of each of the following:

a) 9^2 (F)

....
[1]

b) 4^3 (E)

....
[1]

c) $\sqrt{36}$ (F)

....
[1]

[Total 3 marks]

Score:

6

Prime Numbers, Multiples and Factors

1 Look at the list of numbers below. (E)

$$1 \quad 7 \quad 11 \quad 12 \quad 15 \quad 21$$

a) Write down a number from the list which is a prime number.

....

[1]

b) Which number in the list is a multiple of 5?

....

[1]

c) Write down a number from the list which is a factor of 30 and is greater than 5.

....

[1]

d) Write down two numbers from the list whose sum is a prime number.

.... and ....

[1]

[Total 4 marks]

2 Write down: (E)

a) **all** the factors of 20,

....

[2]

b) all the multiples of 8 which appear in the list below.

$$55 \quad 56 \quad 57 \quad 58 \quad 59 \quad 60 \quad 61 \quad 62 \quad 63 \quad 64 \quad 65$$

....

[1]

[Total 3 marks]

3 Write down: (E)

a) two multiples of 21,

.... , ...

[1]

b) a prime number between 45 and 50.

....

[1]

[Total 2 marks]

Score:

9

Prime Factors, LCM and HCF

1 Find: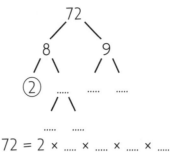

a) 72 as a product of its prime factors.

```
            72
           /  \
          8    9
         / \  / \
        ②  .....  .....  .....
       / \
      .....  .....
```

Make sure your answer only uses prime numbers. Multiply them all together to check you get the number you started with.

72 = 2 × ..... × ..... × ..... × .....

....

[2]

b) the highest common factor (HCF) of 54 and 72.

....

[1]

[Total 3 marks]

2 Two remote-control cars start at the same time from the start line on a track. **C**

One car takes 3 minutes to complete a circuit.
The other car takes 5 minutes to complete a circuit.

If they start side by side, how long will it be before they are next side by side at the start line?

.... minutes

[Total 2 marks]

FUNCTIONAL

3 Phil is making jam. **C**

He needs to buy mini jam jars which come in packs of 35 and lids which come in packs of 55. He doesn't want to have any jars or lids left over.

What is the minimum number of packs of jars he needs to buy?

Multiples of 35 are: 35, 70, ..., ..., ..., ..., ..., ..., ..., ..., ..., ...
Multiples of 55 are: 55, 110, ..., ..., ..., ..., ..., ...

So the LCM is ...., which is the minimum number of jars he needs.
So the minimum number of packs he needs is .... ÷ .... = ... packs

....

[Total 3 marks]

Score:

8

Fractions, Decimals and Percentages

1 Convert each of the following: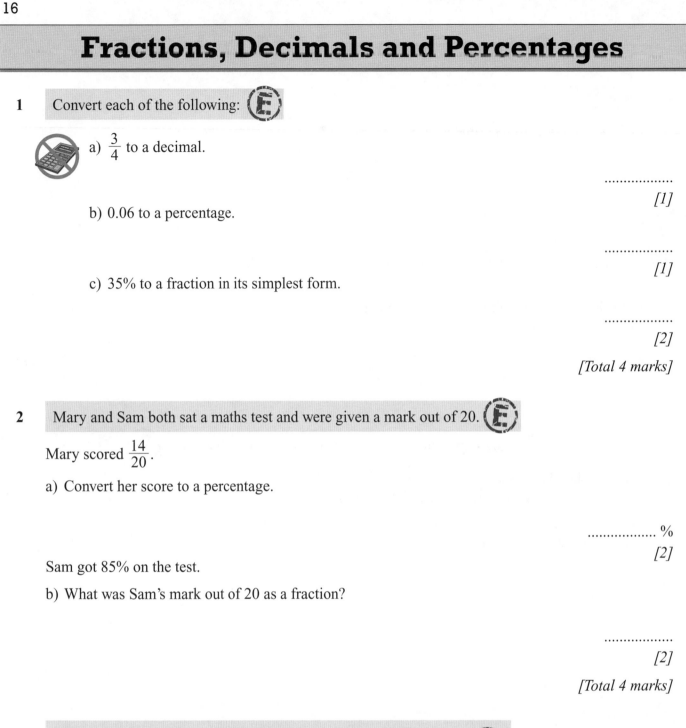

a) $\frac{3}{4}$ to a decimal.

....

[1]

b) 0.06 to a percentage.

....

[1]

c) 35% to a fraction in its simplest form.

....

[2]

[Total 4 marks]

2 Mary and Sam both sat a maths test and were given a mark out of 20.

Mary scored $\frac{14}{20}$.

a) Convert her score to a percentage.

.... %

[2]

Sam got 85% on the test.

b) What was Sam's mark out of 20 as a fraction?

....

[2]

[Total 4 marks]

3 There are 200 guests at a wedding party.
Each guest has either chicken, salmon or a vegetarian main course.

 44% of the guests have chicken.

$\frac{2}{5}$ of the guests have salmon.

How many guests have a vegetarian main course?

....

[Total 3 marks]

Score: ☐

11

☹ ☐   😐 ☐   ☺ ☐

Equivalent Fractions

1 Answer the following questions. (E)

a) Write the fraction $\frac{12}{30}$ in its simplest form.

....
[1]

b) Find the fraction of the shape below which is shaded.
Write this fraction in its simplest form.

....
[2]

c) Shade $\frac{4}{5}$ of the shape to the right.

[1]

[Total 4 marks]

2 Convert each of the following: (D)

a) $\frac{18}{7}$ to a mixed number.

....
[1]

b) $1\frac{3}{4}$ to an improper fraction.

....
[1]

[Total 2 marks]

3 Use the lists of fractions below to answer the following questions. (D)

a) Give the **two** fractions from the list below that are not equivalent to $\frac{1}{3}$

$\frac{3}{9}$ $\frac{2}{6}$ $\frac{3}{12}$ $\frac{5}{15}$ $\frac{6}{20}$ $\frac{8}{24}$

....
[2]

b) Which fraction in the following list is the largest?

$\frac{4}{5}$ $\frac{7}{9}$ $\frac{13}{15}$

You must show your working.

$\frac{4}{5} = \frac{......}{45}$ $\frac{7}{9} = \frac{......}{......}$ $\frac{13}{15} = \frac{......}{......}$

....
[3]

[Total 5 marks]

Score:

11

Fractions

1   Work out the following: 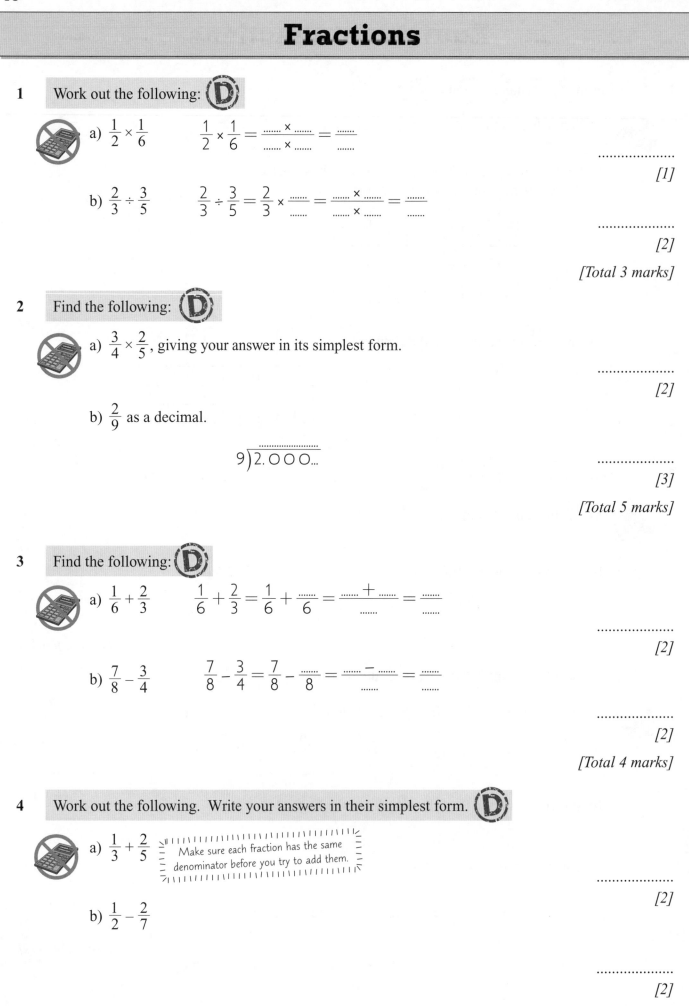 **D**

a) $\frac{1}{2} \times \frac{1}{6}$ $\frac{1}{2} \times \frac{1}{6} = \frac{...... \times ......}{...... \times ......} = \frac{......}{......}$

....

[1]

b) $\frac{2}{3} \div \frac{3}{5}$ $\frac{2}{3} \div \frac{3}{5} = \frac{2}{3} \times \frac{......}{......} = \frac{...... \times ......}{...... \times ......} = \frac{......}{......}$

....

[2]

[Total 3 marks]

2   Find the following: **D**

a) $\frac{3}{4} \times \frac{2}{5}$, giving your answer in its simplest form.

....

[2]

b) $\frac{2}{9}$ as a decimal.

$$9\overline{)2.000...}$$

....

[3]

[Total 5 marks]

3   Find the following: **D**

a) $\frac{1}{6} + \frac{2}{3}$ $\frac{1}{6} + \frac{2}{3} = \frac{1}{6} + \frac{......}{6} = \frac{...... + ...}{......} = \frac{......}{......}$

....

[2]

b) $\frac{7}{8} - \frac{3}{4}$ $\frac{7}{8} - \frac{3}{4} = \frac{7}{8} - \frac{......}{8} = \frac{...... - ......}{......} = \frac{......}{......}$

....

[2]

[Total 4 marks]

4   Work out the following. Write your answers in their simplest form. **D**

a) $\frac{1}{3} + \frac{2}{5}$ Make sure each fraction has the same denominator before you try to add them.

....

[2]

b) $\frac{1}{2} - \frac{2}{7}$

....

[2]

[Total 4 marks]

5 Find: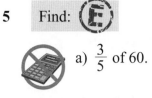

a) $\frac{3}{5}$ of 60.

....
[2]

b) 15 out of 40 as a fraction in its simplest form.

....
[2]

[Total 4 marks]

6 Write down the reciprocal of $\frac{1}{7}$ **C**

....
[Total 1 mark]

7 The turnout at last Saturday's Norchester City game was 12 400.
Season ticket holders made up $\frac{3}{8}$ of the crowd. **D**
How many season ticket holders were there?

....
[Total 2 marks]

8 A school library has £79 to spend on books.
They must spend $\frac{7}{10}$ of the money on non-fiction books and the rest on fiction. **D**

How much must they spend on fiction books?

£ ....
[Total 3 marks]

Section One — Numbers

FUNCTIONAL

*9 Chris is buying a car. The car dealer offers him two different ways to pay. **D**

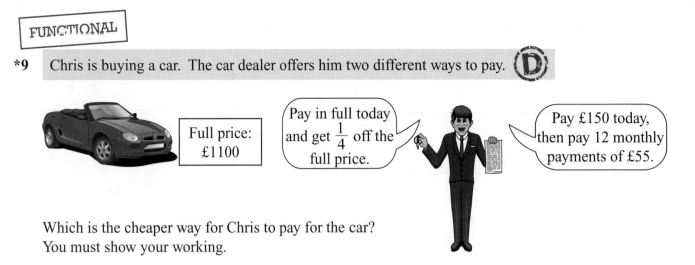

Full price: £1100

Pay in full today and get $\frac{1}{4}$ off the full price.

Pay £150 today, then pay 12 monthly payments of £55.

Which is the cheaper way for Chris to pay for the car?
You must show your working.

[Total 4 marks]

FUNCTIONAL

10 Mr Fletcher owns a farm. It cover 36 acres. He uses $\frac{5}{12}$ of his land for wheat. $\frac{1}{3}$ of the land has cows grazing on it. $\frac{1}{6}$ of the land is used to house pigs. The remaining $\frac{1}{12}$ of the land is taken up by the farmhouse and garden. **C**

It costs him £400 per year for each acre of land used for wheat, cows or pigs.

For each acre used for wheat, he makes £1100 per year.
For each acre used for cows, he makes £1450 per year.
For each acre used for pigs, he makes £1250 per year.

Work out Mr Fletcher's total profit per year.

£ ....

[Total 4 marks]

Score:

34

Proportion Problems

1   Brown sauce can be bought in three different sizes.
    The price of each is shown on the right.
    Which size of bottle is the best value for money?

| 250 ml | 330 ml | 500 ml |
| £2.30 | £2.97 | £4.10 |

.... ml

[Total 2 marks]

2   Cat is baking some muffins for an event in her village hall.
    The list of ingredients below will make 20 muffins.

Ingredients
175 **g** flour (plain)
175 **g** butter
120 **g** sugar
2½ **tsp** baking powder
4 eggs (medium)

Cat wants to make enough muffins for 70 people.

Work out how much she will need of each ingredient.

Flour: (175 ÷ 20) × 70 = ... g

Butter: (............. ÷ 20) × 70 = ... g

Sugar: (............. ÷ ....) × .... = ... g

Baking powder: (............. ÷ ....) × .... = ... tsp

Eggs: (............. ÷ ....) × .... = ...

Flour: .... g

Butter: .... g

Sugar: .... g

Baking powder: .... tsp

Eggs: ....

[Total 3 marks]

Exam Practice Tip

Proportion is really just all about multiplying and dividing — in general, it's quite likely that you can answer
questions on proportion (like the ones on this page) by finding the amount/cost for "one thing" and then either
using this to compare the different options, or multiplying it by the number of things you need.

Score

5

Percentages

1 Aled wants to buy a suitcase to take on holiday. (**D**)

He sees a suitcase which was £18, but today it has 10% off.
a) How much money would he get off the suitcase if he bought it today?

£ ....
[2]

He sees another suitcase which was £24, but the ticket says today the price is reduced by £6.
b) What is £6 as a percentage of £24?

.... %
[2]

[Total 4 marks]

2 Jamila puts £200 into a bank account which earns her 3% simple interest per annum. (**D**)
How much interest will she have earned after 4 years?

3% = 3 ÷ .... = ...

3% of £200 = ... × £200 = £ ....

Interest after 4 years = ... × £ .... = £ ....

£ ....
[Total 3 marks]

3 Jane owns a fashion shop.

Jane sells a pair of jeans for £33.25 plus VAT at 20%.
a) How much does she sell the pair of jeans for? (**D**)

£ ....
[3]

A new style of dress arrives for her to sell.
If she sells each dress for £29, she will make a profit of £6.38 per dress.
b) Calculate the profit as a percentage of the sale price. (**C**)

.... %
[2]

Jane bought a range of necklaces last year for £200, but only sold them for a total of £175.
c) Work out Jane's loss on the range of necklaces as a percentage. (**C**)

.... %
[3]

[Total 8 marks]

4   Liam has just got a new job as a climbing instructor, with a yearly salary of £16 000. Ⓓ
Use the table below to calculate how much tax he will pay each year.

Salary	Income Tax
up to £9440	0% (Tax Free Allowance)
over £9440	20% (on anything above £9440)

£ ....

[Total 3 marks]

5   Bill collects elephant ornaments. Ⓓ

60% of the ornaments are made from wood.
30% of the ornaments are made from stone.

Bill has 3 other elephant ornaments which are made from other materials.
How many elephant ornaments does Bill have in total?

100% − (.......... % + ... %) = ... %

.... % of the total number of elephants = ...

Total number of elephants = (.......... ÷ ....) × 100

= ....

....

[Total 4 marks]

FUNCTIONAL

***6**   John buys broken computers, fixes them and then sells them on. Ⓒ

He bought 20 broken computers for £50 each. He then spent £20 fixing each one.
He gave them a selling price so that he made a profit of 40% on the **total** he had spent per computer.
He sold 12 computers at this price.
He then reduced this price by 12% and sold the remaining 8 computers.

How much profit or loss did John make? Show your working clearly.

[Total 8 marks]

Exam Practice Tip

There are two key things to remember for percentage questions in the exam. To find a percentage of an amount, turn the percentage into a decimal (by dividing by 100), then multiply this by the amount.
To find one amount as a percentage of another, divide the first amount by the second, then multiply by 100.

Score

30

😞 ☐   😐 ☐   🙂 ☐

Ratios

1 Give the ratio 4 : 12 in its simplest form.

....

[Total 1 mark]

2 In a class of 26 children, 12 are boys and 14 are girls.

a) What is the ratio of boys to girls? Give your answer in its simplest form.

....

[1]

b) In another class, the ratio of boys to girls is 2 : 3. There are 25 children in the class. How many girls are there?

....

[2]

[Total 3 marks]

FUNCTIONAL

3 Brian is making a fruit punch. He mixes orange juice, pineapple juice and lemonade in the ratio 4 : 3 : 7. He makes 700 ml of fruit punch.

 What volume of each drink does he use?

Hint: start by trying to find the volume of one "part".

1 part = 700 ÷ (......... + ... + ...)

= 700 ÷ ....

= .... ml

Orange juice: .... × 4 = ... ml
Pineapple juice: .... × .... = ... ml
Lemonade: .... × .... = ... ml

Orange juice: .... ml

Pineapple juice: .... ml

Lemonade: .... ml

[Total 3 marks]

4 Andy, Louise and Christine have £160. They share it in the ratio 3:6:7.

 How much money did Christine get?

£ ....
[Total 2 marks]

5 Last month a museum received £21 000 in donations.
They spent two thirds of the money on heating and lighting.
The rest of the money was spent on staff training and new exhibits in the ratio 2:5.

How much did they spend on new exhibits?

£ ....
[Total 3 marks]

6 Bryn, Heather and Richard have just finished playing a game.

The ratio of Bryn's points to Richard's was 7:4.
Bryn scored 12 more points than Richard.
Heather scored 5 more points than Richard.
Find the number of points each of them scored.

Bryn scored 12 more points than Richard,
so 12 points = 7 parts − 4 parts = 3 parts

1 part = ... ÷ .... = ... points

Richard's score = ... × 4 = ... points

Bryn's score = ... + 12 = ... points

Heather's score = ... + ... = ... points

Bryn: .... points

Heather: .... points

Richard: .... points
[Total 3 marks]

Score:

15

Section One — Numbers

Rounding Off and Estimating Calculations

1   Round the following to the given degree of accuracy.

a) Josh has 123 people coming to his party. (F)
Write this number to the nearest 10.

....

[1]

b) The attendance at a football match was 2568 people. (F)
What is this to the nearest hundred?

....

[1]

c) The population of Ulverpool is 452 529. (E)
Round this to the nearest 100 000.

....

[1]

[Total 3 marks]

2   The distance between two stars is 428.6237 light years.

a) Round this distance to one decimal place. (E)

.... light years

[1]

b) Round this distance to 2 significant figures. (D)

.... light years

[1]

[Total 2 marks]

3   Use your calculator to find: (D)

$$\frac{4.32^2 - \sqrt{13.4}}{16.3 + 2.19}$$

Give your answer to 3 significant figures.

....

[Total 2 marks]

4   Estimate the value of $\dfrac{12.2 \times 1.86}{0.19}$ (C)

You should start by rounding each number to an easier one.

....

[Total 3 marks]

Score: ☐

10

Powers and Roots

1   Use your calculator to find the following: 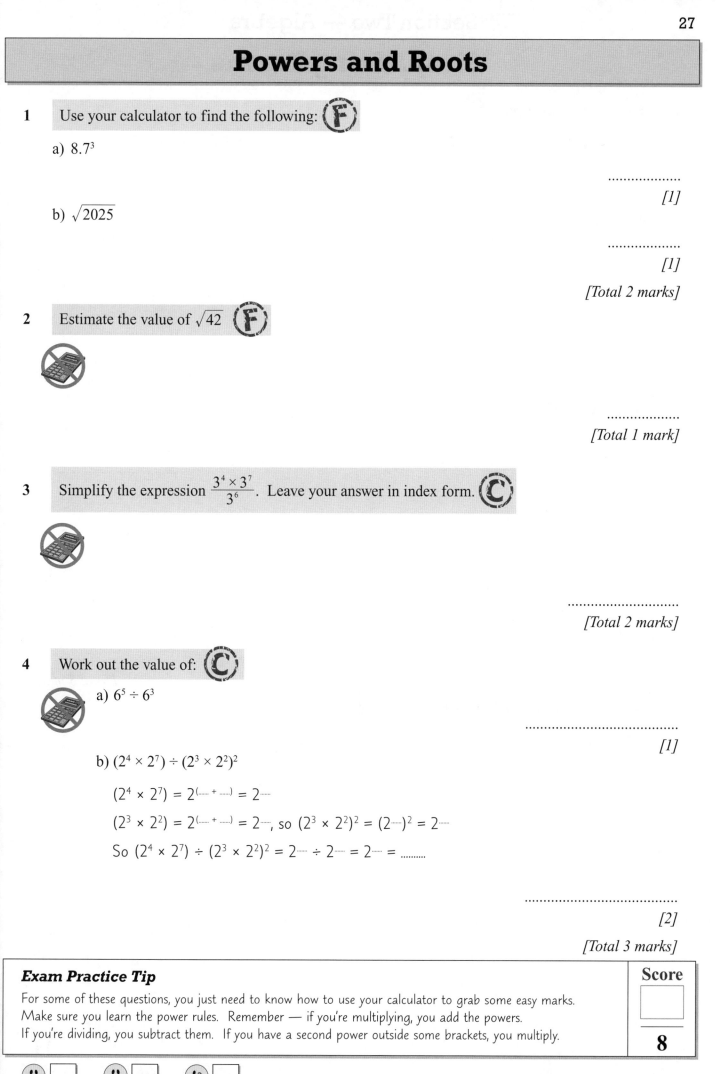 **F**

a) 8.7^3

....

[1]

b) $\sqrt{2025}$

....

[1]

[Total 2 marks]

2   Estimate the value of $\sqrt{42}$ **F**

....

[Total 1 mark]

3   Simplify the expression $\dfrac{3^4 \times 3^7}{3^6}$. Leave your answer in index form. **C**

....

[Total 2 marks]

4   Work out the value of: **C**

a) $6^5 \div 6^3$

....

[1]

b) $(2^4 \times 2^7) \div (2^3 \times 2^2)^2$

$(2^4 \times 2^7) = 2^{(\text{......} + \text{......})} = 2^{\text{......}}$

$(2^3 \times 2^2) = 2^{(\text{......} + \text{......})} = 2^{\text{......}}$, so $(2^3 \times 2^2)^2 = (2^{\text{......}})^2 = 2^{\text{......}}$

So $(2^4 \times 2^7) \div (2^3 \times 2^2)^2 = 2^{\text{......}} \div 2^{\text{......}} = 2^{\text{......}} = $ ....

....

[2]

[Total 3 marks]

Exam Practice Tip

For some of these questions, you just need to know how to use your calculator to grab some easy marks. Make sure you learn the power rules. Remember — if you're multiplying, you add the powers. If you're dividing, you subtract them. If you have a second power outside some brackets, you multiply.

Score

8

Simplifying Terms

1   Simplify the following.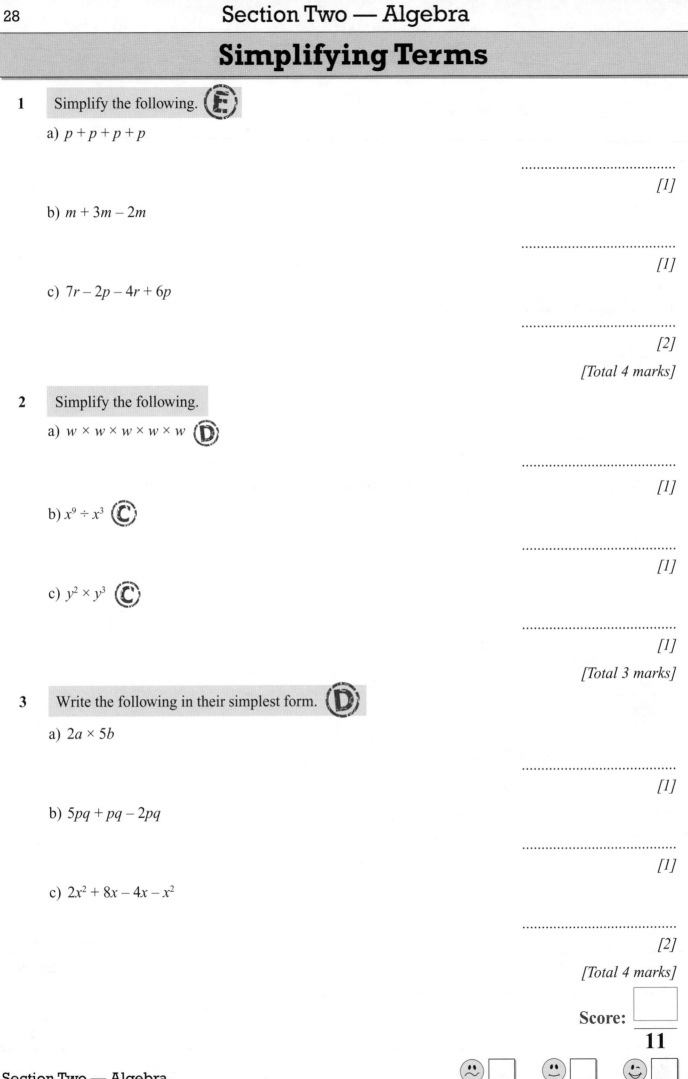

a) $p + p + p + p$

....

[1]

b) $m + 3m - 2m$

....

[1]

c) $7r - 2p - 4r + 6p$

....

[2]

[Total 4 marks]

2   Simplify the following.

a) $w \times w \times w \times w \times w$

....

[1]

b) $x^9 \div x^3$

....

[1]

c) $y^2 \times y^3$

....

[1]

[Total 3 marks]

3   Write the following in their simplest form.

a) $2a \times 5b$

....

[1]

b) $5pq + pq - 2pq$

....

[1]

c) $2x^2 + 8x - 4x - x^2$

....

[2]

[Total 4 marks]

Score:

11

Multiplying Out Brackets

1 Expand the following. (C)

a) $3(x-2)$

= (3 × ....) + (3 × ....) = ... − ....

....
[1]

b) $x(x+4)$

....
[1]
[Total 2 marks]

2 Multiply out the brackets and simplify where possible. (C)

a) $5(x+y)$

....
[1]

b) $s(2s-3)$

....
[1]

c) $2a(2a+3)$

= (2a × ....) + (2a × ....) = ... + ...

....
[1]

d) $2b-3(b-1)$

....
[2]
[Total 5 marks]

3 Expand and simplify where possible. (C)

a) $3(x-1)+5(x+2)$

....
[2]

b) $4a(a+2b)$

....
[1]

c) $9-3(x+2)$

....
[2]
[Total 5 marks]

Score: ⬚

12

Taking Out Common Factors

1   Factorise the following expressions.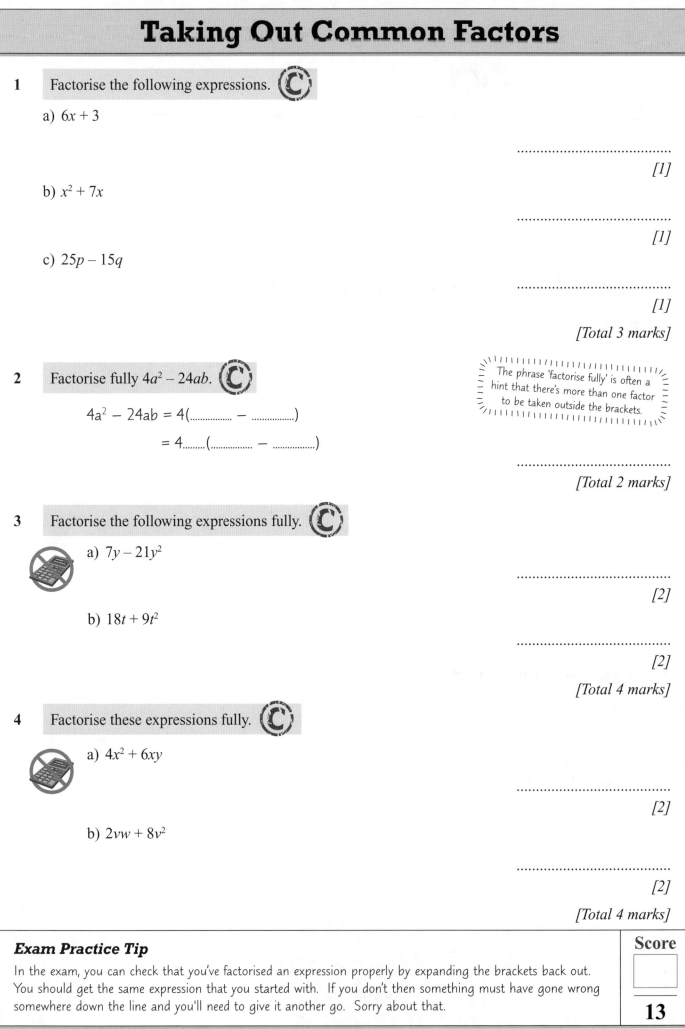

a) $6x + 3$

....

[1]

b) $x^2 + 7x$

....

[1]

c) $25p - 15q$

....

[1]

[Total 3 marks]

2   Factorise fully $4a^2 - 24ab$.

$$4a^2 - 24ab = 4(\text{..............} - \text{................})$$
$$= 4\text{........}(\text{.............} - \text{................})$$

> The phrase 'factorise fully' is often a hint that there's more than one factor to be taken outside the brackets.

....

[Total 2 marks]

3   Factorise the following expressions fully.

a) $7y - 21y^2$

....

[2]

b) $18t + 9t^2$

....

[2]

[Total 4 marks]

4   Factorise these expressions fully.

a) $4x^2 + 6xy$

....

[2]

b) $2vw + 8v^2$

....

[2]

[Total 4 marks]

Exam Practice Tip

In the exam, you can check that you've factorised an expression properly by expanding the brackets back out. You should get the same expression that you started with. If you don't then something must have gone wrong somewhere down the line and you'll need to give it another go. Sorry about that.

Score

13

Solving Equations

1   Solve these equations for x.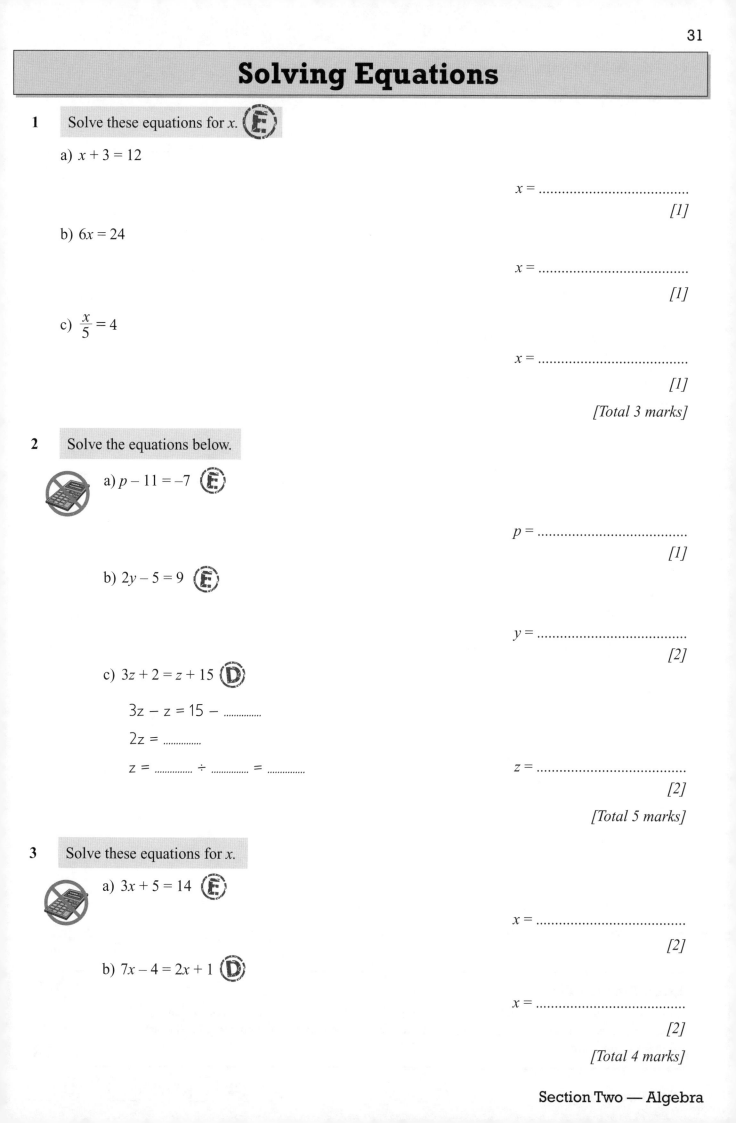

a) $x + 3 = 12$

$x =$ ....

[1]

b) $6x = 24$

$x =$ ....

[1]

c) $\dfrac{x}{5} = 4$

$x =$ ....

[1]

[Total 3 marks]

2   Solve the equations below.

a) $p - 11 = -7$

$p =$ ....

[1]

b) $2y - 5 = 9$

$y =$ ....

[2]

c) $3z + 2 = z + 15$

$3z - z = 15 -$ ....

$2z =$ ....

$z =$ .... $\div$ .... $=$ ....

$z =$ ....

[2]

[Total 5 marks]

3   Solve these equations for x.

a) $3x + 5 = 14$

$x =$ ....

[2]

b) $7x - 4 = 2x + 1$

$x =$ ....

[2]

[Total 4 marks]

4 Solve the following equations. **D**

a) $40 - 3x = 17x$

$x = $ ....
[2]

b) $2y - 5 = 3y - 12$

$y = $ ....
[2]

[Total 4 marks]

5 Find the solution to each of the following equations. **C**

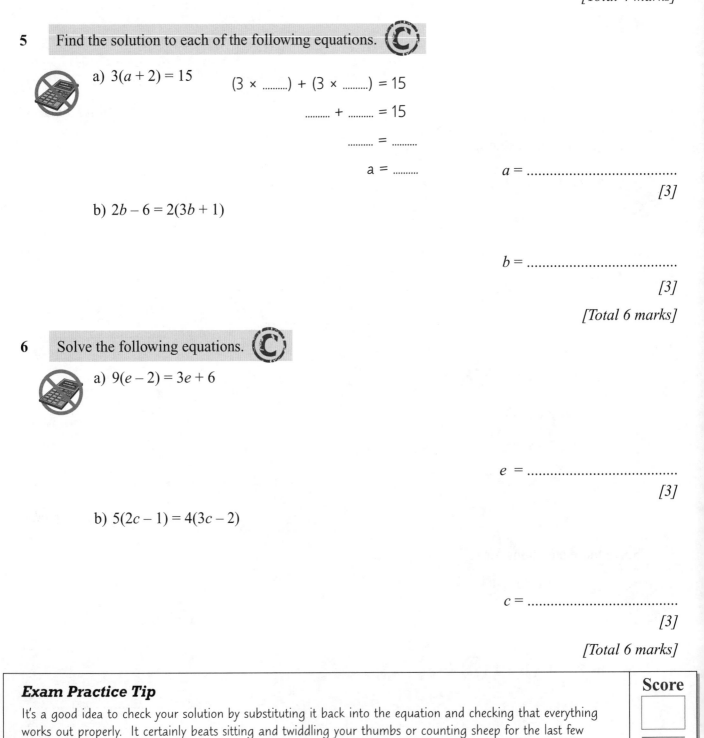

a) $3(a + 2) = 15$

$(3 \times$ ....$) + (3 \times$ ....$) = 15$

.... + ... $= 15$

.... $=$ ....

$a = $ ....

$a = $ ....
[3]

b) $2b - 6 = 2(3b + 1)$

$b = $ ....
[3]

[Total 6 marks]

6 Solve the following equations. **C**

a) $9(e - 2) = 3e + 6$

$e = $ ....
[3]

b) $5(2c - 1) = 4(3c - 2)$

$c = $ ....
[3]

[Total 6 marks]

Exam Practice Tip

It's a good idea to check your solution by substituting it back into the equation and checking that everything works out properly. It certainly beats sitting and twiddling your thumbs or counting sheep for the last few minutes of your exam.

Score

28

Writing Equations

1   Alexa is playing a number game.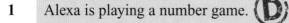

Alexa thinks of a number and multiplies it by 7. She subtracts 12 from this new number.
Her answer is equal to 4 times her original number.

What was her original number?

....

[Total 2 marks]

2   *ABC* is an equilateral triangle and *EFGH* is a rectangle. Ⓒ
      ABC and *EFGH* have the same perimeter.

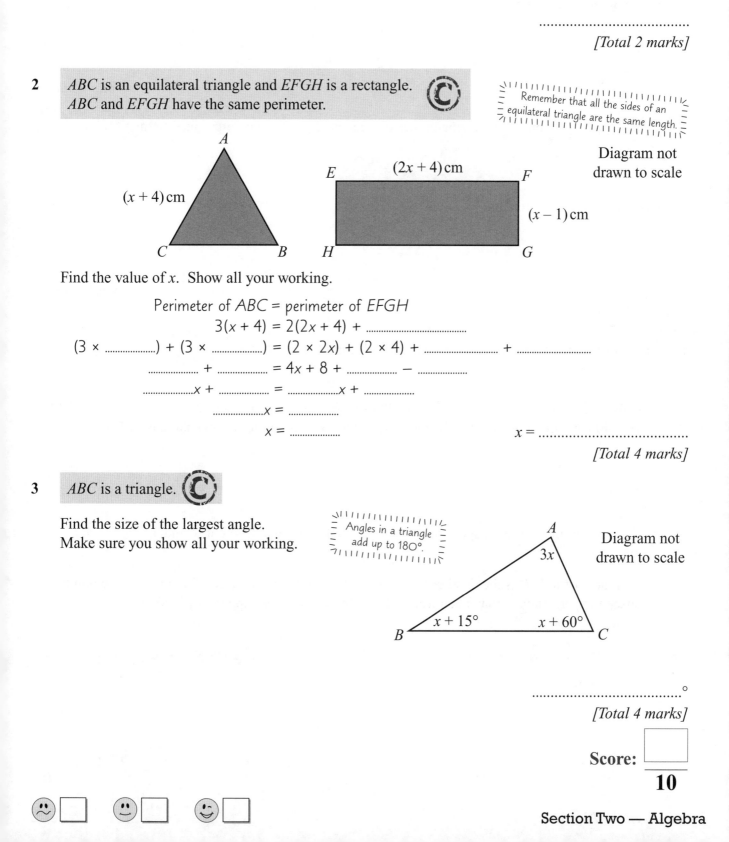

Remember that all the sides of an equilateral triangle are the same length.

Diagram not drawn to scale

E $(2x + 4)$ cm   *F*

$(x + 4)$ cm

$(x - 1)$ cm

Find the value of x. Show all your working.

Perimeter of ABC = perimeter of EFGH

$$3(x + 4) = 2(2x + 4) + \text{.................}$$

$$(3 \times \text{.............}) + (3 \times \text{.............}) = (2 \times 2x) + (2 \times 4) + \text{.................} + \text{.................}$$

$$\text{.............} + \text{.............} = 4x + 8 + \text{.................} - \text{.................}$$

$$\text{.............}x + \text{.............} = \text{.............}x + \text{.............}$$

$$\text{.............}x = \text{.............}$$

$$x = \text{.............}$$

$$x = \text{.................................}$$

[Total 4 marks]

3   *ABC* is a triangle. Ⓒ

Find the size of the largest angle.
Make sure you show all your working.

Angles in a triangle add up to 180°.

Diagram not drawn to scale

A

$3x$

$x + 15°$ $x + 60°$

B   *C*

.................................°

[Total 4 marks]

Score:

10

😞 ☐   😐 ☐   🙂 ☐

Using Formulas

1 $Q = 7x - 3y$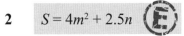

Find the value of Q when $x = 8$ and $y = 7$.

....

[Total 2 marks]

2 $S = 4m^2 + 2.5n$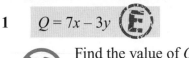

Calculate the value of S when $m = 6.5$ and $n = 4$.

S = (4 × .... × ....) + (2.5 × ....)

S = ... + ...

S = ...

....

[Total 2 marks]

3   The formula for converting a temperature in Celsius (C) to a temperature in Fahrenheit (F) is:

$$F = \frac{9C}{5} + 32$$

Convert 35 °C to Fahrenheit.

.... °F

[Total 2 marks]

FUNCTIONAL

4   The cost of hiring a bouncy castle is calculated using the formula below.

$$C = S + 7H$$

C is the cost in £, S is the charge in £ to set the castle up and H is the number of hours it is hired for.

a) How much will it cost to hire a bouncy castle for 13 hours if the set-up charge is £25?

£ ....

[2]

b) The cost of hiring a set of space hoppers is calculated using a different formula:

$$C = 2H + 5N$$

C is the cost in £, H is the number of hours the space hoppers are hired for, and N is the number of space hoppers hired. How much would it cost to hire 5 space hoppers for 3 hours?

£ ....

[2]

[Total 4 marks]

Score:

10

Writing and Rearranging Formulas

1   To hire a cement mixer, Alex pays £50 per day plus a flat fee of £300. (E)

a) Write a formula to show the total cost C (in £) of hiring the cement mixer for d days.

Total cost = flat fee + (cost per day × number of days)

$C =$ .... + (.................. × ....)

$C =$ .... + ...

....

[2]

b) How much would Alex have to pay to hire the cement mixer for 3 days?

£................................

[2]

[Total 4 marks]

2   To convert kilometres into miles, Tasmin says that you divide (E) the number of kilometres by 8 and multiply the answer by 5.

a) Write this rule as a formula.
Use k to represent the number of kilometres and m to represent the number of miles.

....

[2]

b) Use your formula to convert 110 kilometres into miles.

.... miles

[2]

[Total 4 marks]

3   Len and Sam have been shopping for books. (E)

a) Len spent m pounds more than Sam.
If Sam spent v pounds, write an expression to show how much Len spent.

....

[1]

b) Each page of one of the books is 0.1 mm thick.
The front and back covers are both 3 mm thick.
Write a formula to show the total thickness t (in mm) of a book with x pages.

....

[2]

[Total 3 marks]

4 A furniture delivery company charges a flat fee of £35 per delivery, plus an additional £10 for each piece of furniture.

a) Write a formula giving the total cost A (in £) of a delivery of F pieces of furniture.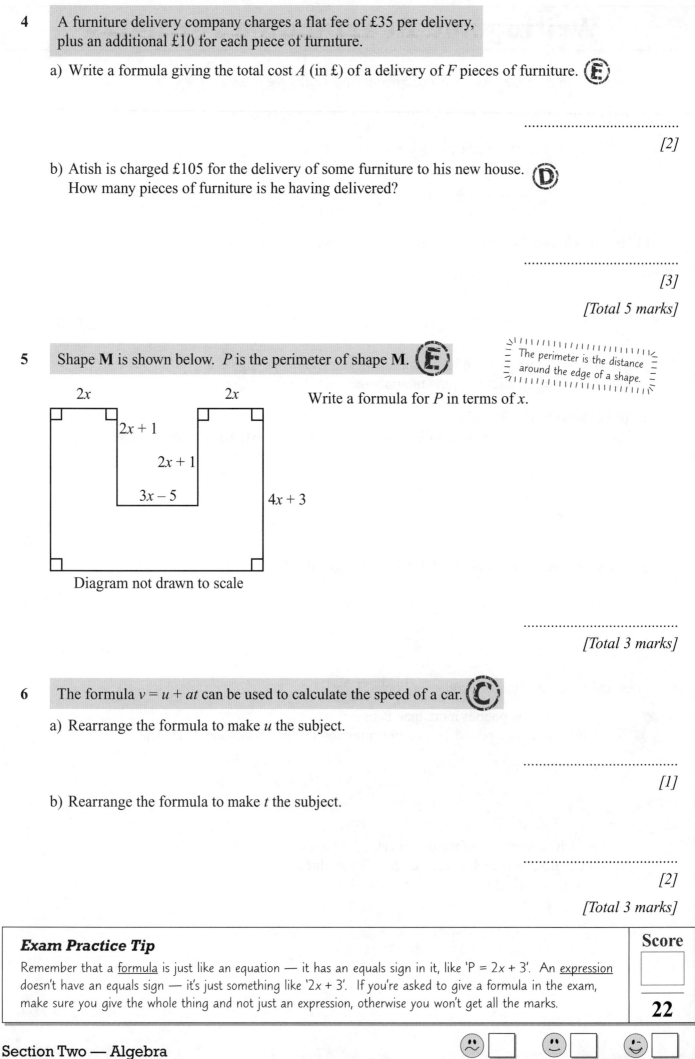

....
[2]

b) Atish is charged £105 for the delivery of some furniture to his new house. How many pieces of furniture is he having delivered?

....
[3]

[Total 5 marks]

5 Shape **M** is shown below. P is the perimeter of shape **M**.

> The perimeter is the distance around the edge of a shape.

Write a formula for P in terms of x.

2x   2x

2x + 1

2x + 1

3x − 5

4x + 3

Diagram not drawn to scale

....

[Total 3 marks]

6 The formula $v = u + at$ can be used to calculate the speed of a car.

a) Rearrange the formula to make u the subject.

....
[1]

b) Rearrange the formula to make t the subject.

....
[2]

[Total 3 marks]

Exam Practice Tip

Remember that a <u>formula</u> is just like an equation — it has an equals sign in it, like 'P = 2x + 3'. An <u>expression</u> doesn't have an equals sign — it's just something like '2x + 3'. If you're asked to give a formula in the exam, make sure you give the whole thing and not just an expression, otherwise you won't get all the marks.

Score

22

Number Patterns and Sequences

1 Here are the first four terms of an arithmetic sequence. (E)

      4   12   20   28

a) Write down the next two terms in the sequence.

.... and ....

[1]

b) The 25th term in the sequence is 196. Write down the 23rd term in the sequence.

....

[1]

c) Thomas says that the 12th term is 90. Explain why he is incorrect.

....

....

[2]

[Total 4 marks]

2 Fill in the gaps in the following sequences, and give the rule for each sequence. (E)

a)   13   18   23   33   ....

Rule: ....

[2]

b)   6   12   24   48   ....

Rule: ....

[2]

[Total 4 marks]

3 A sequence is made from patterns of triangles. The first three patterns are shown below. (E)

a) Draw the fourth pattern in the sequence.

[1]

b) How many small triangles are there in the ninth pattern in the sequence?
Give a reason for your answer.

....

[2]

[Total 3 marks]

Section Two — Algebra

4 A sequence is made of patterns of straight lines and circles. (E)

Pattern 1   Pattern 2   Pattern 3

a) Write down the number of circles in Pattern 8.

....

[1]

b) Work out the number of straight lines in the pattern containing 22 circles.

....

[2]

[Total 3 marks]

5 The first four terms in a sequence are 2, 9, 16, 23, ... (C)

a) Find the *n*th term of the sequence.

2   9   16   23

....

The common difference is ...., so ....n is in the formula.

n = 1   2   ....

........n = ...

↓   ↓   ↓   ↓

nth term = ...

You have to subtract .... to get to the term.

So the expression for the nth term is ....n − ....

....

[2]

b) What is the 30th term of the sequence?

....

[1]

[Total 3 marks]

6 This question is about the sequence 3, 7, 11, 15, 19... (C)

Find the *n*th term of the sequence.

....

[Total 2 marks]

Score:

19

Trial and Improvement

1   The equation $x^3 + 4x = 24$ has a solution between 2 and 3. **C**

Find this solution.
Give your answer correct to 1 decimal place and show all your working.

x	$x^3 + 4x$	
2	$2^3 + (4 \times 2) = 8 + 8 = 16$	Too small
3	$3^3 + (4 \times 3) = \text{............} + \text{............} = \text{............}$	....

$x = $ ....

[Total 4 marks]

2   The equation $x^3 - 2x = 0$ has a solution between 1 and 2. **C**

Find this solution to 1 decimal place.
Use the trial and improvement method and show your working.

$x = $ ....

[Total 4 marks]

Exam Practice Tip	**Score**
Make sure that you learn the method for solving trial and improvement problems — don't go randomly plugging in numbers all over the place. It's really important that you show all your working — the examiner needs to see that you've been systematic and tried all the values you're supposed to have done.	8

Inequalities

1   Write down the inequality shown on the number line below.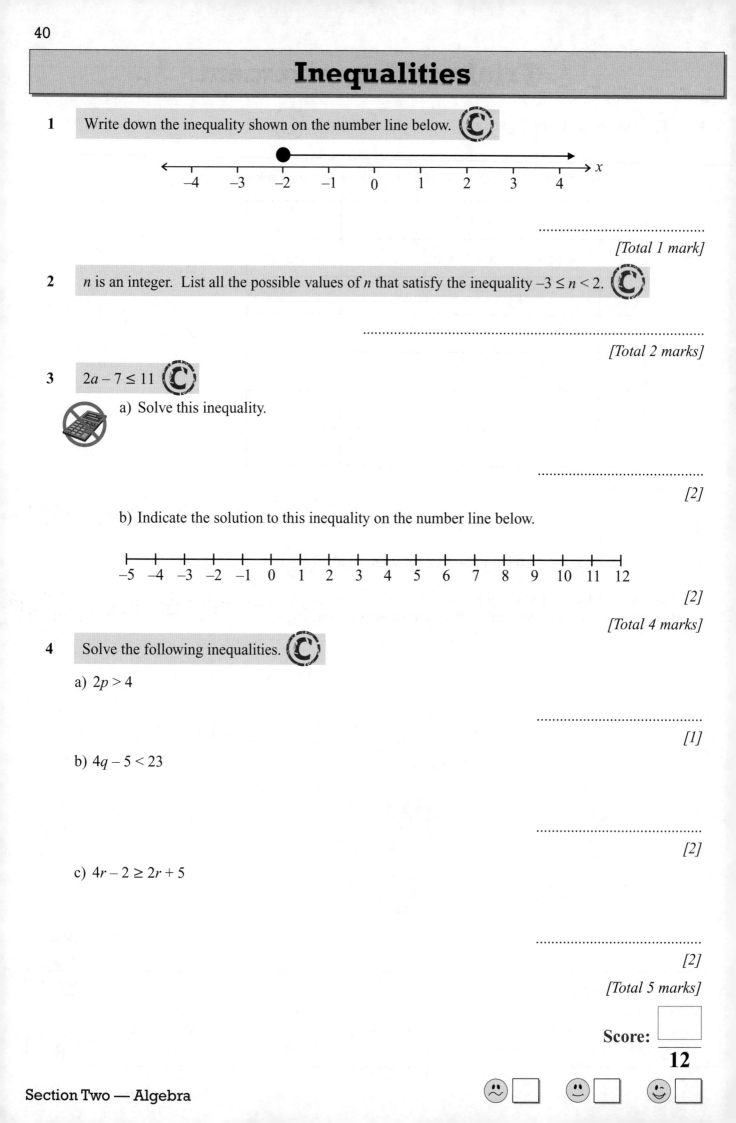

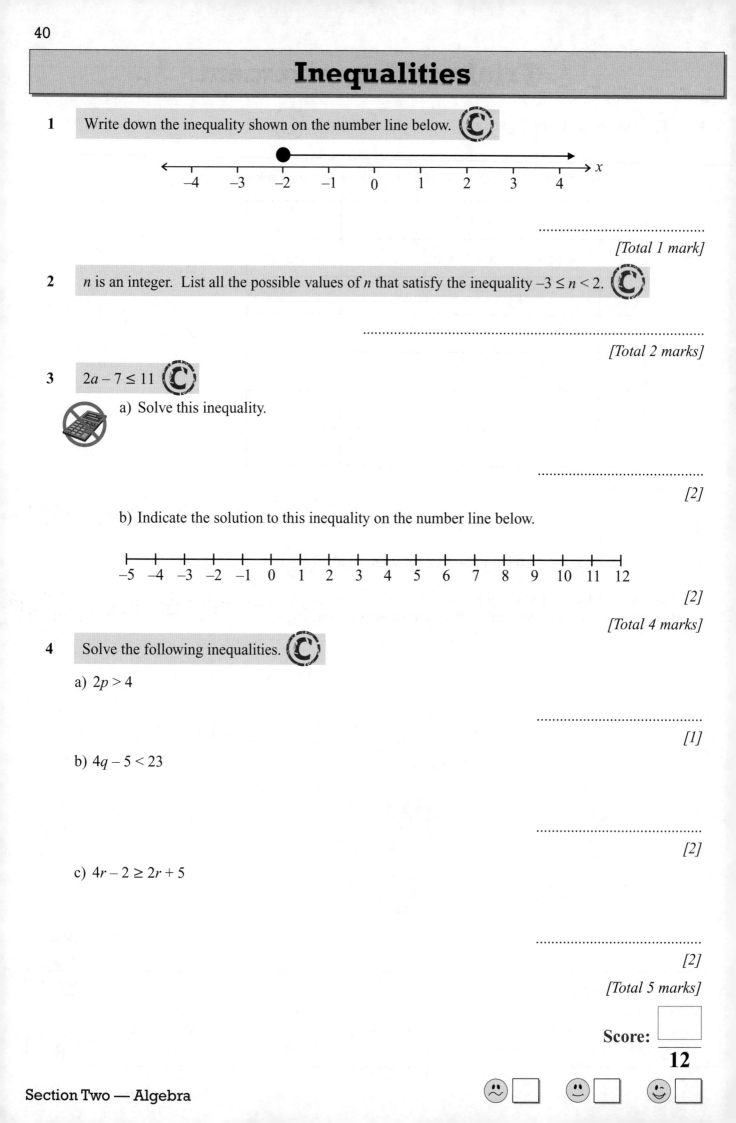

....

[Total 1 mark]

2   *n* is an integer. List all the possible values of *n* that satisfy the inequality $-3 \leq n < 2$.

....

[Total 2 marks]

3   $2a - 7 \leq 11$

a) Solve this inequality.

....

[2]

b) Indicate the solution to this inequality on the number line below.

[2]

[Total 4 marks]

4   Solve the following inequalities.

a) $2p > 4$

....

[1]

b) $4q - 5 < 23$

....

[2]

c) $4r - 2 \geq 2r + 5$

....

[2]

[Total 5 marks]

Score:

12

Coordinates and Midpoints

1   Two points have been plotted on the grid below. They are labelled **A** and **B**. (F)

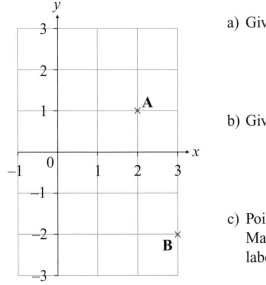

a) Give the coordinates of point **A**.

(..............., ...)

[1]

b) Give the coordinates of point **B**.

(..............., ...)

[1]

c) Point **C** has the coordinates (1, −1).
Mark this point on the grid on the left using a cross (×) and label it **C**.

[1]

[Total 3 marks]

2   Points **Q** and **R** have been plotted on the grid below.

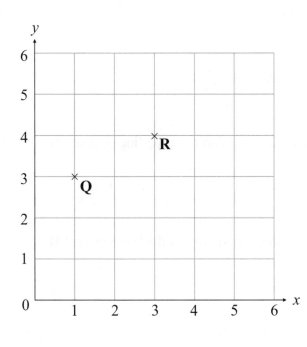

a) What are the coordinates of point **Q**? (F)

(..............., ...)

[1]

b) Point **S** lies on the *x*-axis.
The line **QS** is parallel to the *y*-axis. (E)
What are the coordinates of point **S**?

(..............., ...)

[2]

c) Point **T** lies on the *y*-axis.
The line **TR** is parallel to the *x*-axis. (E)
What are the coordinates of point **T**?

(..............., ...)

[2]

[Total 5 marks]

3 Ⓒ

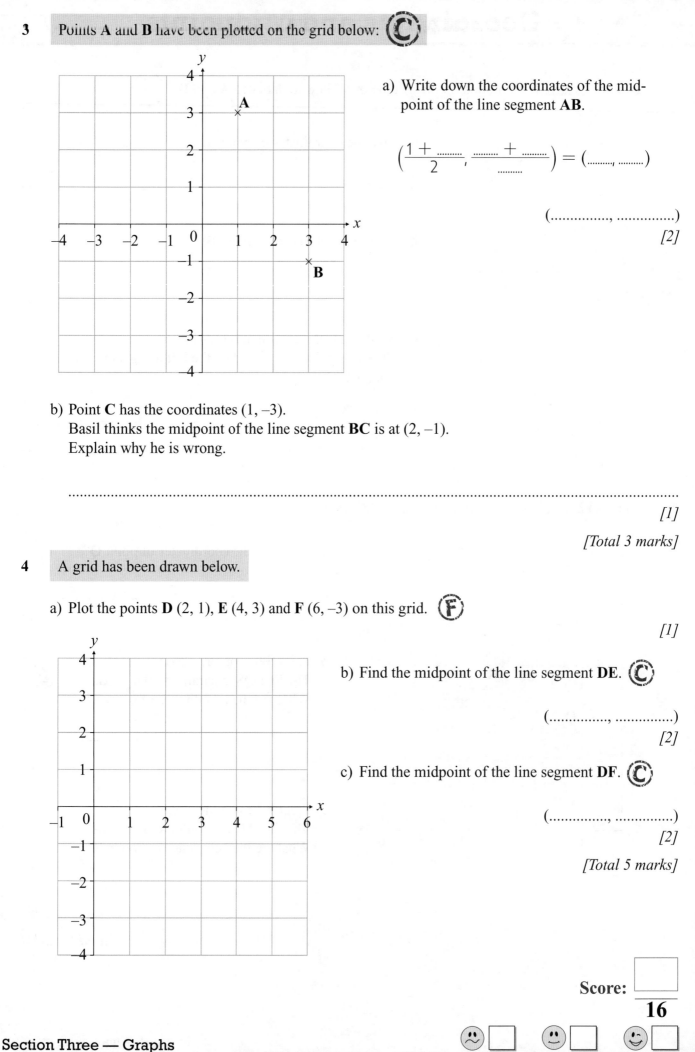

a) Write down the coordinates of the mid-point of the line segment **AB**.

$$\left(\frac{1 + \text{.........}}{2}, \frac{\text{.........} + \text{.........}}{\text{.........}}\right) = (\text{........, ...})$$

(.............., ...)
[2]

b) Point **C** has the coordinates $(1, -3)$.
Basil thinks the midpoint of the line segment **BC** is at $(2, -1)$.
Explain why he is wrong.

....

[1]

[Total 3 marks]

4 A grid has been drawn below.

a) Plot the points **D** $(2, 1)$, **E** $(4, 3)$ and **F** $(6, -3)$ on this grid. Ⓕ

[1]

b) Find the midpoint of the line segment **DE**. Ⓒ

(.............., ...)
[2]

c) Find the midpoint of the line segment **DF**. Ⓒ

(.............., ...)
[2]

[Total 5 marks]

Score:

16

Straight-Line Graphs

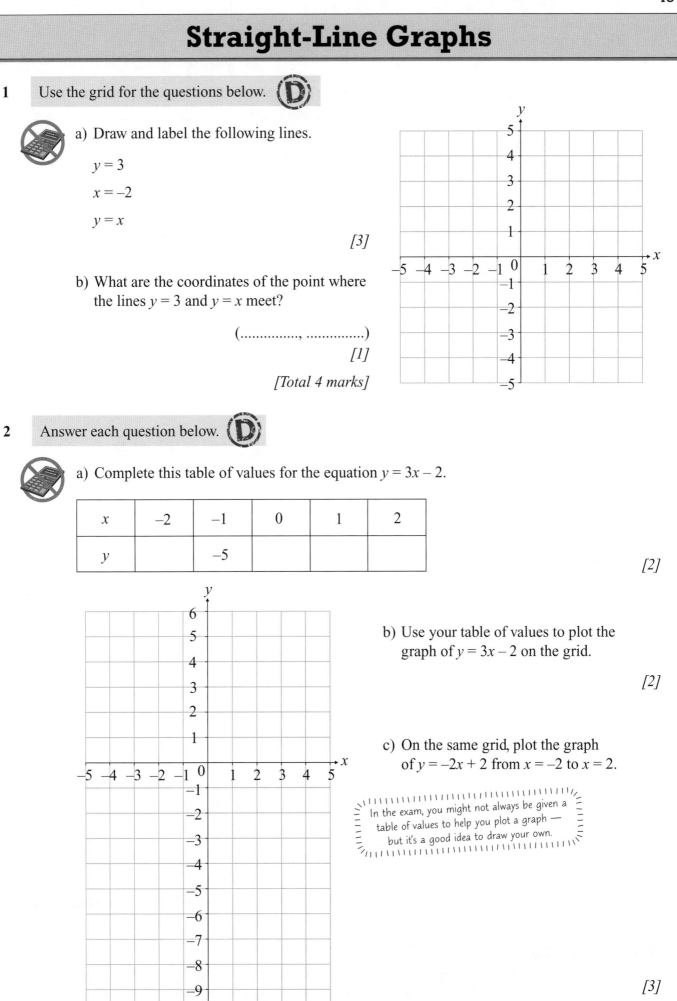

1 Use the grid for the questions below. **D**

a) Draw and label the following lines.

$y = 3$

$x = -2$

$y = x$

[3]

b) What are the coordinates of the point where the lines $y = 3$ and $y = x$ meet?

(..............., ...)

[1]

[Total 4 marks]

2 Answer each question below. **D**

a) Complete this table of values for the equation $y = 3x - 2$.

x	-2	-1	0	1	2
y		-5			

[2]

b) Use your table of values to plot the graph of $y = 3x - 2$ on the grid.

[2]

c) On the same grid, plot the graph of $y = -2x + 2$ from $x = -2$ to $x = 2$.

In the exam, you might not always be given a table of values to help you plot a graph — but it's a good idea to draw your own.

[3]

[Total 7 marks]

3 This is a question about the equation $y = 8 - 3x$. **(D)**

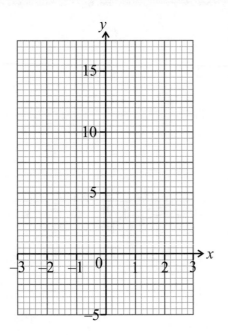

a) Complete this table of values for the equation $y = 8 - 3x$.

x	-2	-1	0	1	2
y				5	

[2]

b) Using the table, draw the graph of
$y = 8 - 3x$ on the grid to the left.

[2]

[Total 4 marks]

4 On the grid below, draw the graph of $2x + y = 6$ for values of x from -4 to 4. **(D)**

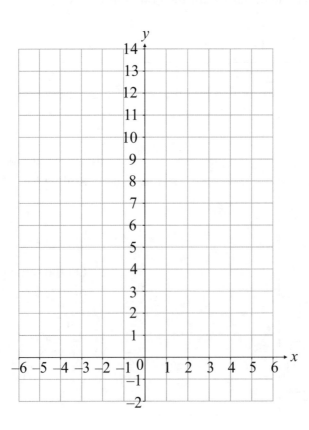

[Total 3 marks]

Exam Practice Tip

When you're drawing straight-line graphs, make sure you always use a ruler — otherwise you'll be throwing away valuable marks in the exam. If one of your points doesn't fit in a straight line with the others, the chances are you've made a mistake filling in your table of values — so it's best to go back and double-check.

Score

18

Travel Graphs

1 The travel graph below shows Selby's bike ride from his house (**A**) to the zoo (**C**), which is 25 km away.

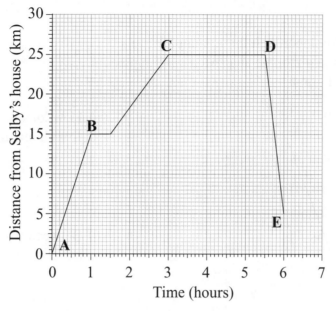

a) After one hour, Selby stops at a bench (**B**) for a rest.
Find the gradient of the line between point **A** and point **B**.

....

[2]

b) What does the gradient of the line between point **A** and point **B** represent?

....

[1]

c) How long was Selby's journey to the zoo (**C**) from home (**A**)?

.... hours

[1]

d) How long did Selby spend at the zoo?

.... hours

[1]

e) After the zoo, Selby stopped at the shops (**E**) for 30 minutes before cycling straight home at a constant speed. Given that he arrived home 7 hours after he had first left, complete the graph above.

[2]

f) How many hours did Selby spend cycling in total during the day?

.... hours

[1]

[Total 8 marks]

2 Marcus lives in Barcastle, 90 miles away from Appleborough. **(D)**

At 12 o'clock midday Marcus left his home and travelled to Appleborough.
The graph below shows his journey to Appleborough.

a) How long did he take to complete the first 40 miles?

.... hours

[1]

b) Marcus stayed in Appleborough for 45 minutes.
He then travelled straight home at a speed of 45 mph.
Complete the travel graph.

Remember: speed = distance ÷ time

[2]

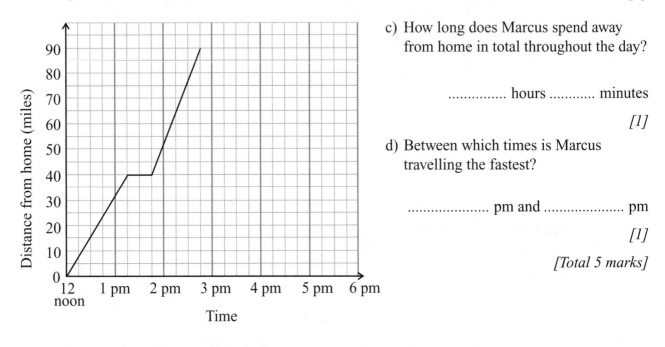

c) How long does Marcus spend away from home in total throughout the day?

.... hours .... minutes

[1]

d) Between which times is Marcus travelling the fastest?

.... pm and .... pm

[1]

[Total 5 marks]

3 Katherine is going to the cinema. **(D)**

She leaves her house at 1 pm and walks at a constant speed of 3.5 mph.
Katherine arrives at the cinema 2 hours later.
She stays for 3 hours and 45 minutes, and then travels straight home by bus.

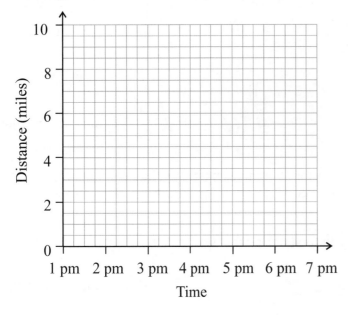

a) Given that Katherine arrives back home at 7 pm, use the grid on the left to draw a distance-time graph showing her journey.

[3]

b) What is Katherine's average speed on the bus home?

.... mph

[2]

[Total 5 marks]

Score:

18

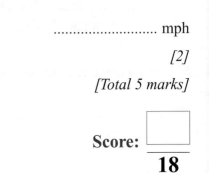

Section Three — Graphs

Conversion Graphs

1   Use the graph to help you answer the questions below.

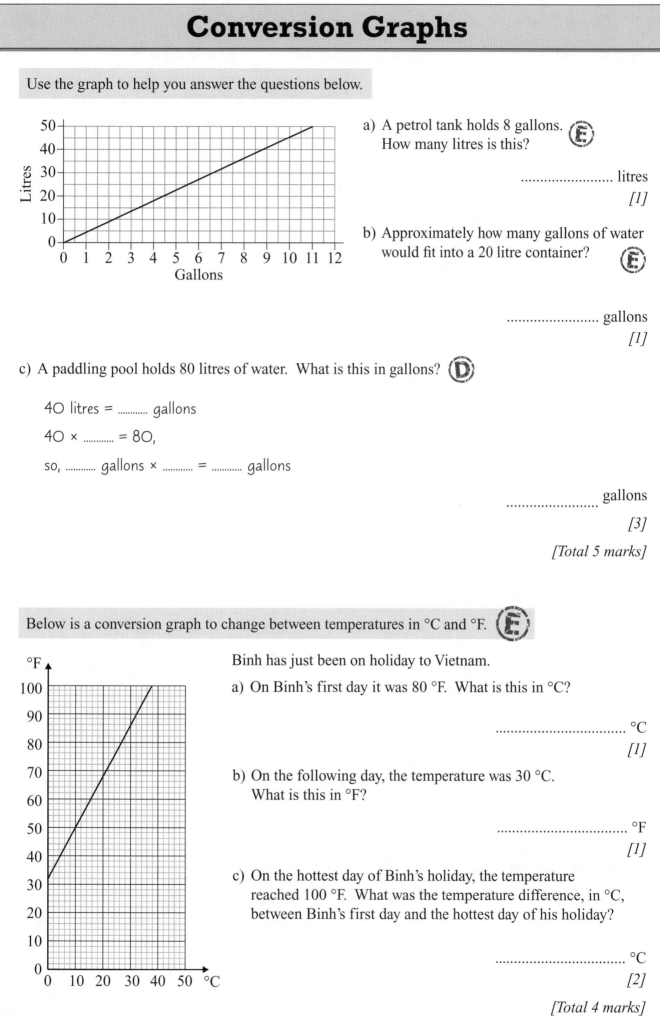

a) A petrol tank holds 8 gallons. **E**
   How many litres is this?

   .... litres
   [1]

b) Approximately how many gallons of water
   would fit into a 20 litre container? **E**

   .... gallons
   [1]

c) A paddling pool holds 80 litres of water. What is this in gallons? **D**

   40 litres = ... gallons

   40 × .... = 80,

   so, ... gallons × .... = ... gallons

   .... gallons
   [3]

   [Total 5 marks]

2   Below is a conversion graph to change between temperatures in °C and °F. **E**

Binh has just been on holiday to Vietnam.

a) On Binh's first day it was 80 °F. What is this in °C?

   .... °C
   [1]

b) On the following day, the temperature was 30 °C.
   What is this in °F?

   .... °F
   [1]

c) On the hottest day of Binh's holiday, the temperature
   reached 100 °F. What was the temperature difference, in °C,
   between Binh's first day and the hottest day of his holiday?

   .... °C
   [2]

   [Total 4 marks]

Section Three — Graphs

*3 Edwige has just returned from a holiday in France.
She compares how much she spent on holiday to what she would normally spend at home.

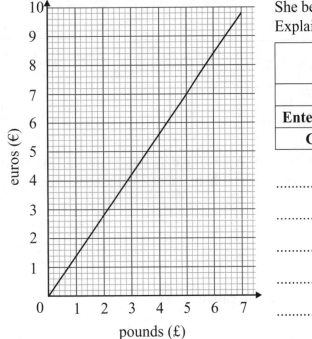

She believes she saved money while on holiday.
Explain why she is correct.

	Holiday spending (€)	Home spending (£)
Food	€50	£30
Entertainment	€70	£50
Clothes	€100	£80

....

....

....

....

....

[Total 5 marks]

4 The graphs below can be used to convert between pounds (lb), kilograms (kg) and stone.

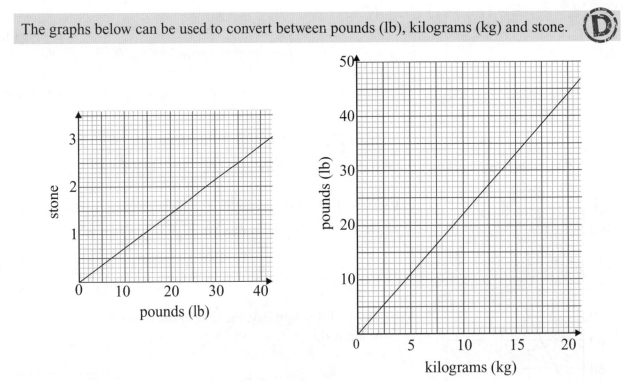

Aston's prize-winning pumpkin weighs 5.5 stone.
Use the graphs above to find the weight of his pumpkin in kilograms.

.... kg

[Total 4 marks]

Score: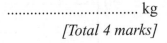

18

Section Three — Graphs

Real-Life Graphs

1   A laundry service charges a flat fee of £5, plus £1 per item washed.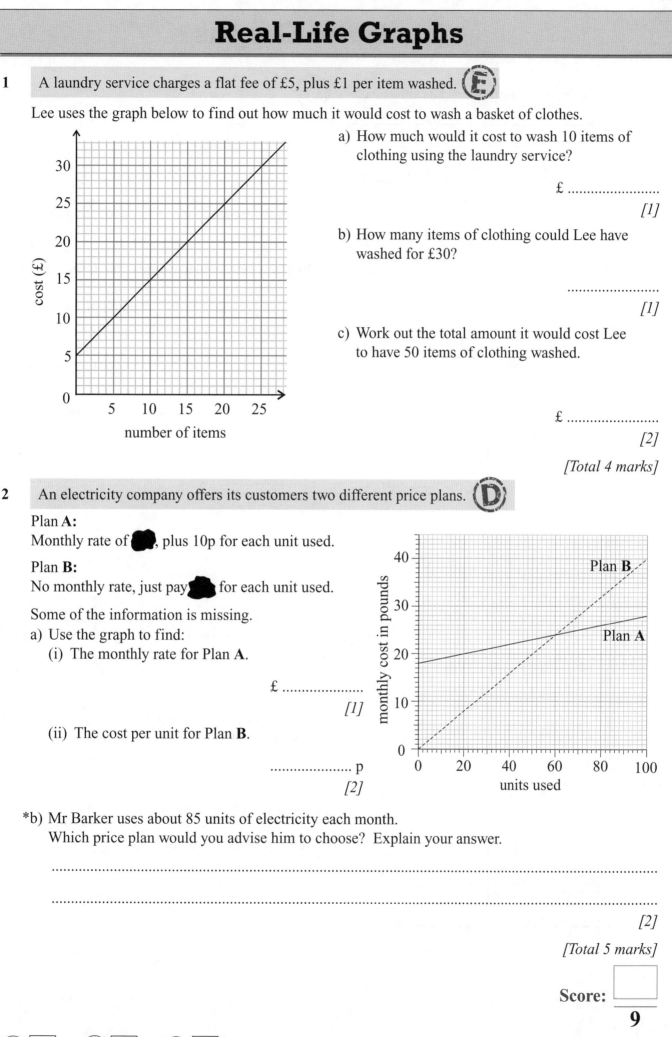

Lee uses the graph below to find out how much it would cost to wash a basket of clothes.

a) How much would it cost to wash 10 items of clothing using the laundry service?

£ ....
[1]

b) How many items of clothing could Lee have washed for £30?

....
[1]

c) Work out the total amount it would cost Lee to have 50 items of clothing washed.

£ ....
[2]

[Total 4 marks]

2   An electricity company offers its customers two different price plans. D

Plan **A:**
Monthly rate of ●, plus 10p for each unit used.

Plan **B:**
No monthly rate, just pay ● for each unit used.

Some of the information is missing.
a) Use the graph to find:
(i) The monthly rate for Plan **A**.

£ ....
[1]

(ii) The cost per unit for Plan **B**.

.... p
[2]

*b) Mr Barker uses about 85 units of electricity each month.
Which price plan would you advise him to choose? Explain your answer.

....

....
[2]

[Total 5 marks]

Score:

9

Quadratic Graphs

1 A table of values for $y = x^2 - 5$ is shown below. ©

x	-3	-2	-1	0	1	2
y	4	-1	-4	-5	-4	-1

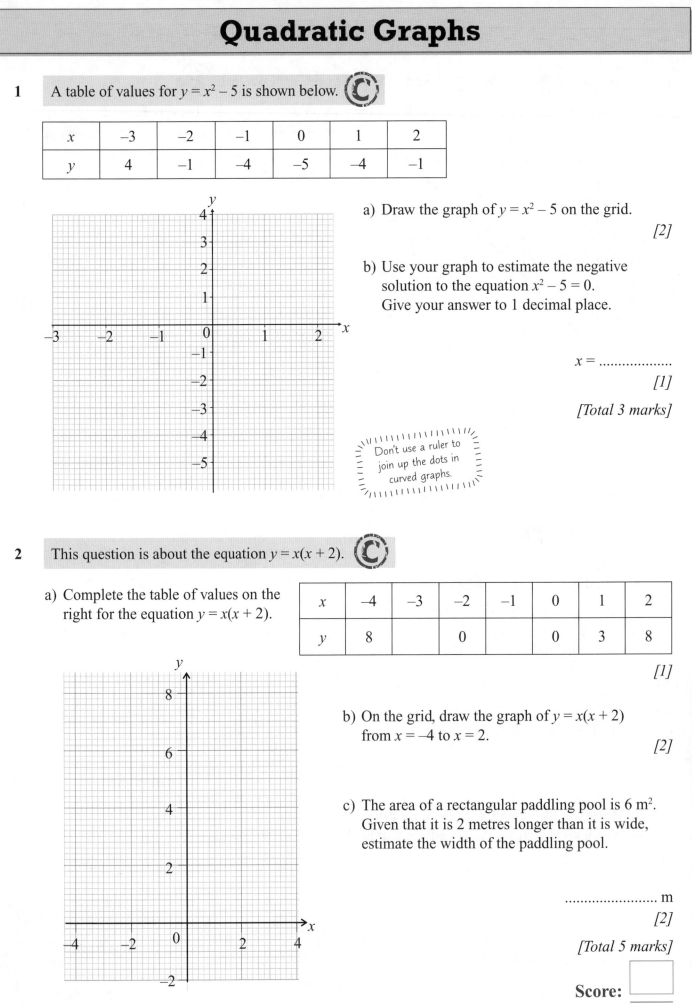

a) Draw the graph of $y = x^2 - 5$ on the grid.

[2]

b) Use your graph to estimate the negative
solution to the equation $x^2 - 5 = 0$.
Give your answer to 1 decimal place.

$x = $ ....

[1]

[Total 3 marks]

Don't use a ruler to join up the dots in curved graphs.

2 This question is about the equation $y = x(x + 2)$. ©

a) Complete the table of values on the
right for the equation $y = x(x + 2)$.

x	-4	-3	-2	-1	0	1	2
y	8		0		0	3	8

[1]

b) On the grid, draw the graph of $y = x(x + 2)$
from $x = -4$ to $x = 2$.

[2]

c) The area of a rectangular paddling pool is 6 m².
Given that it is 2 metres longer than it is wide,
estimate the width of the paddling pool.

.... m

[2]

[Total 5 marks]

Score:

8

Symmetry and Tessellations

1 Below are some incomplete patterns. (F)

a) Shade in four more squares in the grid below so that line AB is a line of symmetry.

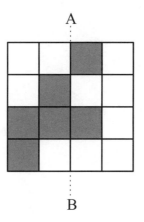

[1]

b) Shade in six more squares so that the grid below has exactly two lines of symmetry.

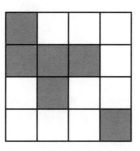

[1]

c) Complete the pattern below so it has rotational symmetry of order 4 around point **A**.

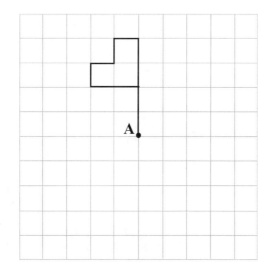

[2]

[Total 4 marks]

2 Each shape below is made with five small squares. (F)

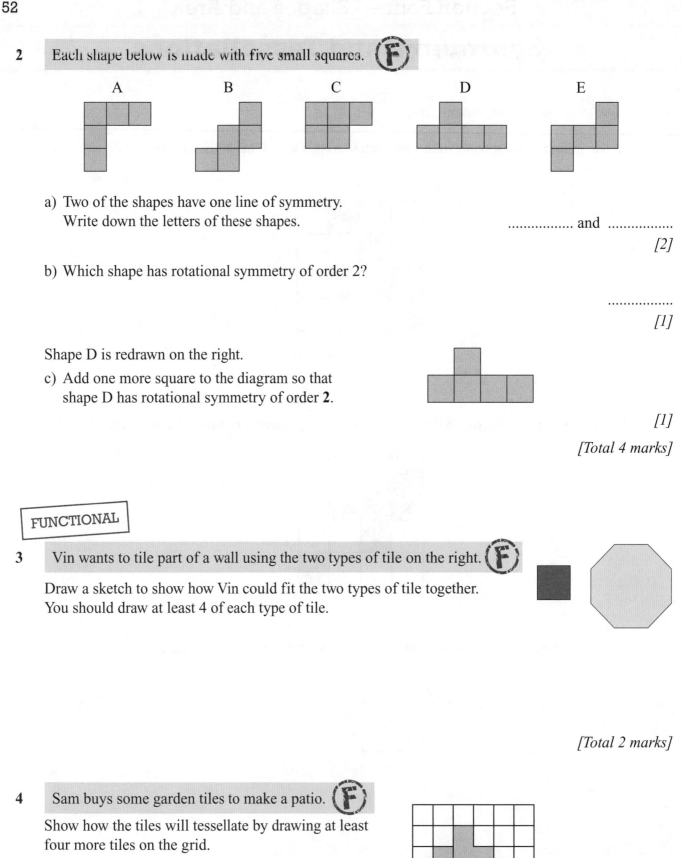

A   B   C   D   E

a) Two of the shapes have one line of symmetry.
Write down the letters of these shapes.

.... and ....
[2]

b) Which shape has rotational symmetry of order 2?

....
[1]

Shape D is redrawn on the right.

c) Add one more square to the diagram so that
shape D has rotational symmetry of order **2**.

[1]

[Total 4 marks]

FUNCTIONAL

3 Vin wants to tile part of a wall using the two types of tile on the right. (F)

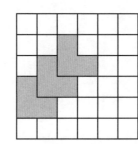

Draw a sketch to show how Vin could fit the two types of tile together.
You should draw at least 4 of each type of tile.

[Total 2 marks]

4 Sam buys some garden tiles to make a patio. (F)

Show how the tiles will tessellate by drawing at least
four more tiles on the grid.

[Total 2 marks]

Score:

12

Properties of 2D Shapes

1 Below are four shapes.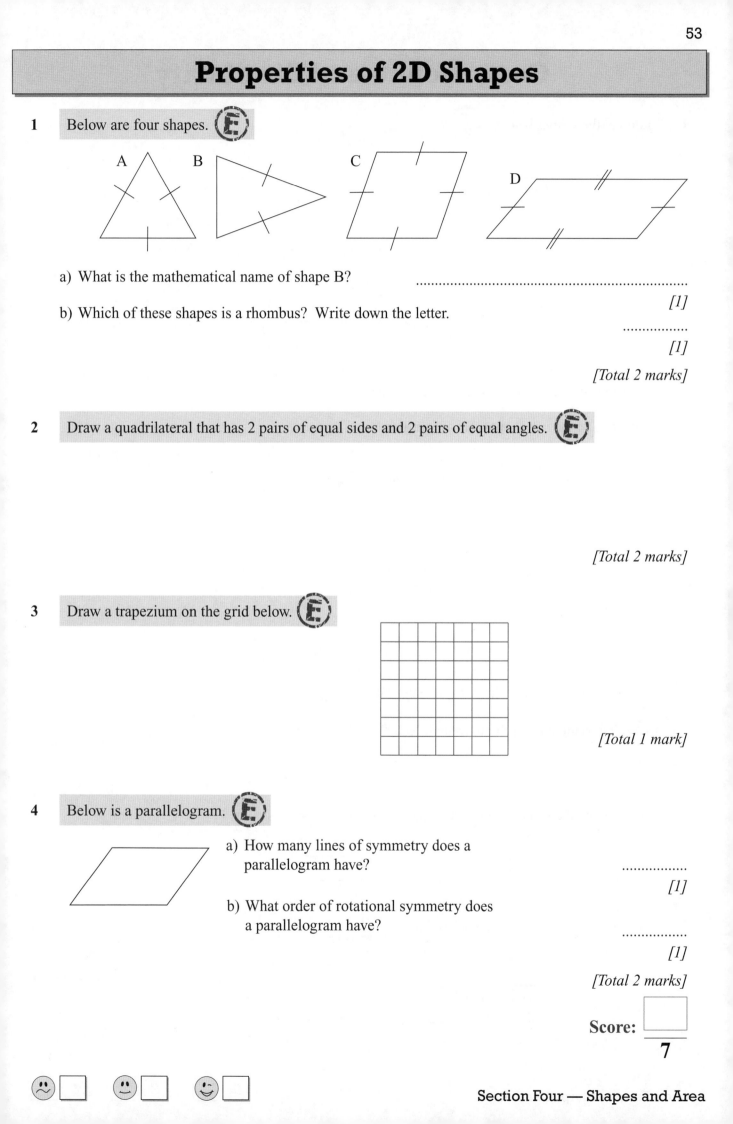

A   B   C   D

a) What is the mathematical name of shape B?   ....

[1]

b) Which of these shapes is a rhombus? Write down the letter.

....

[1]

[Total 2 marks]

2 Draw a quadrilateral that has 2 pairs of equal sides and 2 pairs of equal angles.

[Total 2 marks]

3 Draw a trapezium on the grid below.

[Total 1 mark]

4 Below is a parallelogram.

a) How many lines of symmetry does a
   parallelogram have?

....

[1]

b) What order of rotational symmetry does
   a parallelogram have?

....

[1]

[Total 2 marks]

Score: ☐

7

Congruence and Similarity

1 Look at the shapes below. **(F)**

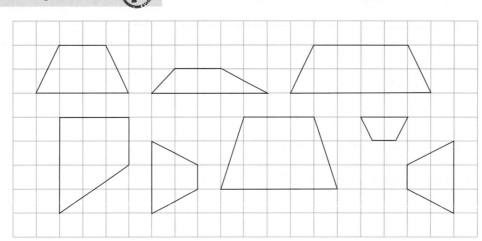

a) Write C in the two shapes that are **congruent**. *[1]*

b) Write S in the two shapes that are **similar**. *[1]*

[Total 2 marks]

2 The shape below has been divided into triangles. **(F)**

a) Which triangle in this diagram is congruent to triangle *ABY*?

....

[1]

b) Which triangle is similar to triangle *ACD*?

....

[1]

[Total 2 marks]

3 Write down the letters of 2 different pairs of congruent shapes. **(F)**

.... and ....

.... and ....

[Total 2 marks]

Score: ☐

6

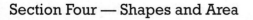

3D Shapes

1   Write down the mathematical names of the 3D shapes below. **G**

A _____

[1]

B _____

[1]

[Total 2 marks]

2   Thomas is making toffee for Christmas presents. **F**

He wants to make boxes to put his toffee in.
He works out that he needs a cuboid as
shown on the right.

How many of the following does the cuboid have?

a) Faces

....

[1]

b) Edges

....

[1]

c) Vertices

....

[1]

[Total 3 marks]

3   Below are four 3D shapes. **F**

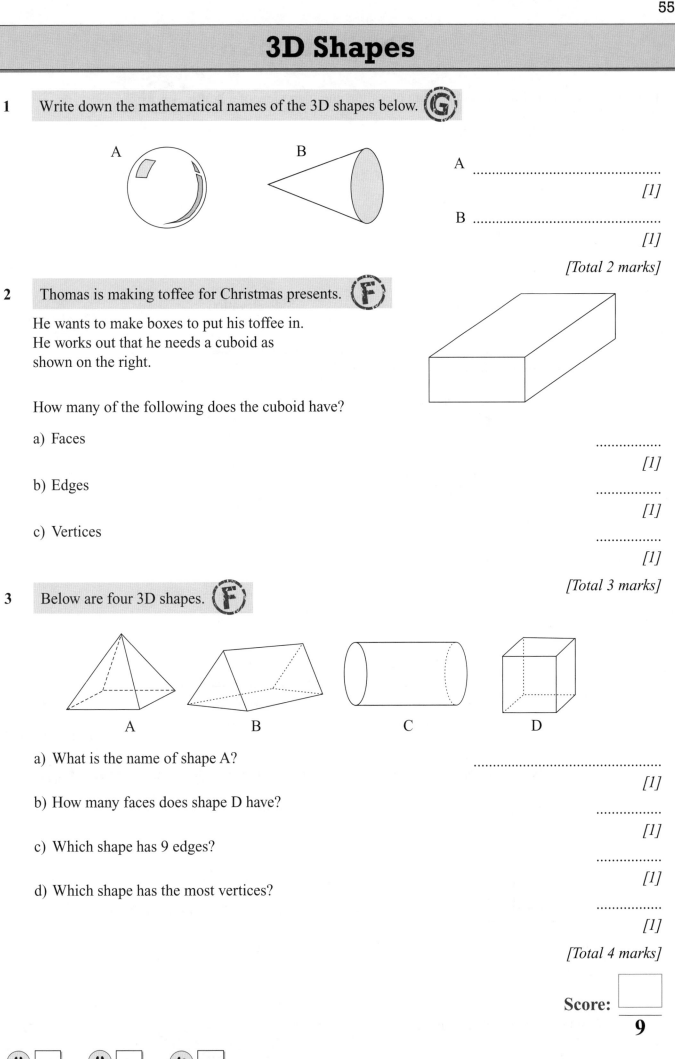

A   B   C   D

a) What is the name of shape A?

....

[1]

b) How many faces does shape D have?

....

[1]

c) Which shape has 9 edges?

....

[1]

d) Which shape has the most vertices?

....

[1]

[Total 4 marks]

Score:

9

Projections

1   The diagram below shows the front elevation and plan view of a house. **D**

Draw the side elevation of the house.

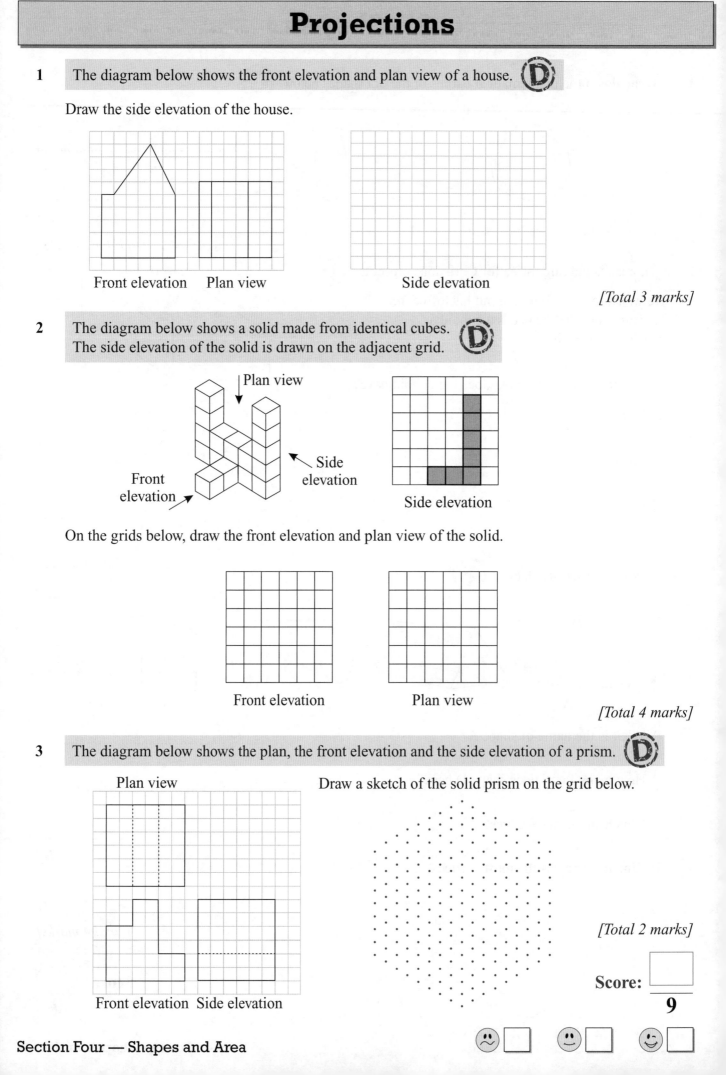

Front elevation   Plan view   Side elevation

[Total 3 marks]

2   The diagram below shows a solid made from identical cubes. **D**
The side elevation of the solid is drawn on the adjacent grid.

Plan view

Side elevation

Front elevation

Side elevation

On the grids below, draw the front elevation and plan view of the solid.

Front elevation   Plan view

[Total 4 marks]

3   The diagram below shows the plan, the front elevation and the side elevation of a prism. **D**

Plan view

Draw a sketch of the solid prism on the grid below.

Front elevation   Side elevation

[Total 2 marks]

Score:

9

Section Four — Shapes and Area

Perimeters and Areas

1 The shape below is drawn on a grid of centimetre squares.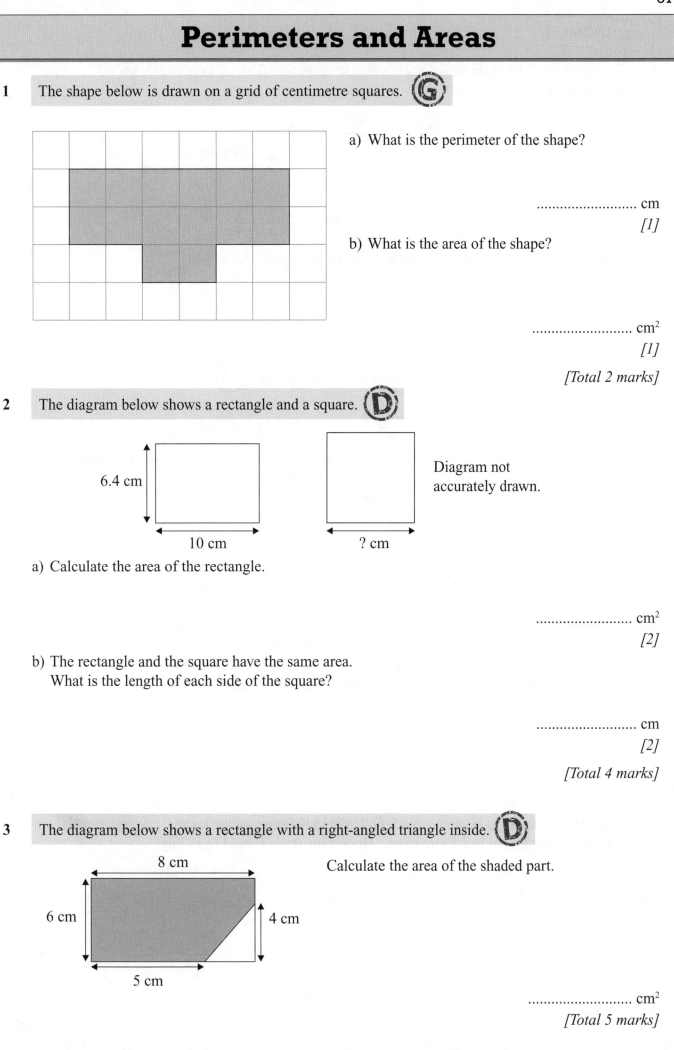

a) What is the perimeter of the shape?

.... cm
[1]

b) What is the area of the shape?

.... cm²
[1]

[Total 2 marks]

2 The diagram below shows a rectangle and a square.

6.4 cm

10 cm

? cm

Diagram not accurately drawn.

a) Calculate the area of the rectangle.

.... cm²
[2]

b) The rectangle and the square have the same area.
What is the length of each side of the square?

.... cm
[2]

[Total 4 marks]

3 The diagram below shows a rectangle with a right-angled triangle inside.

8 cm

6 cm

4 cm

5 cm

Calculate the area of the shaded part.

.... cm²
[Total 5 marks]

Section Four — Shapes and Area

4 The diagram shows a field. A farmer wants to spray weedkiller on the field. **D** Weedkiller costs £0.27 per 10 m².

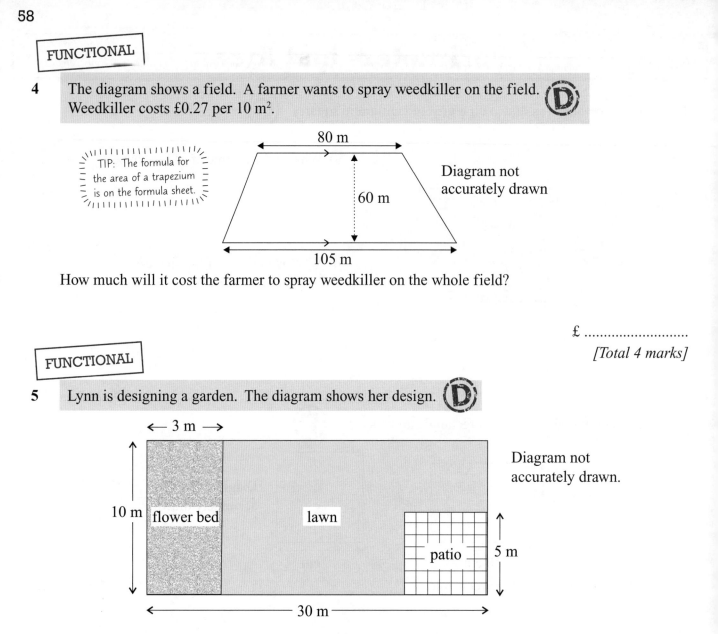

TIP: The formula for the area of a trapezium is on the formula sheet.

80 m

60 m

105 m

Diagram not accurately drawn

How much will it cost the farmer to spray weedkiller on the whole field?

£ ....

[Total 4 marks]

5 Lynn is designing a garden. The diagram shows her design. **D**

← 3 m →

10 m | flower bed | lawn | patio | 5 m

30 m

Diagram not accurately drawn.

Lynn's garden will be rectangular, with a rectangular flower bed at one end, and a square patio at the other end. The rest of the space is taken up by a lawn.

a) The grass seed that Lynn is planning to use comes in boxes that cost £7 each. Each box will cover 10 m². How much will it cost Lynn to plant the lawn?

£ ....

[6]

b) Lynn wants to put a decorative border all around the edges of the lawn. Lawn edging is sold in 2 metre strips. How many strips should Lynn buy?

....

[3]

[Total 9 marks]

Score:

24

Section Four — Shapes and Area

Circles

1 The diagram shows a circle with centre O.
A, B and C are points on the circle.

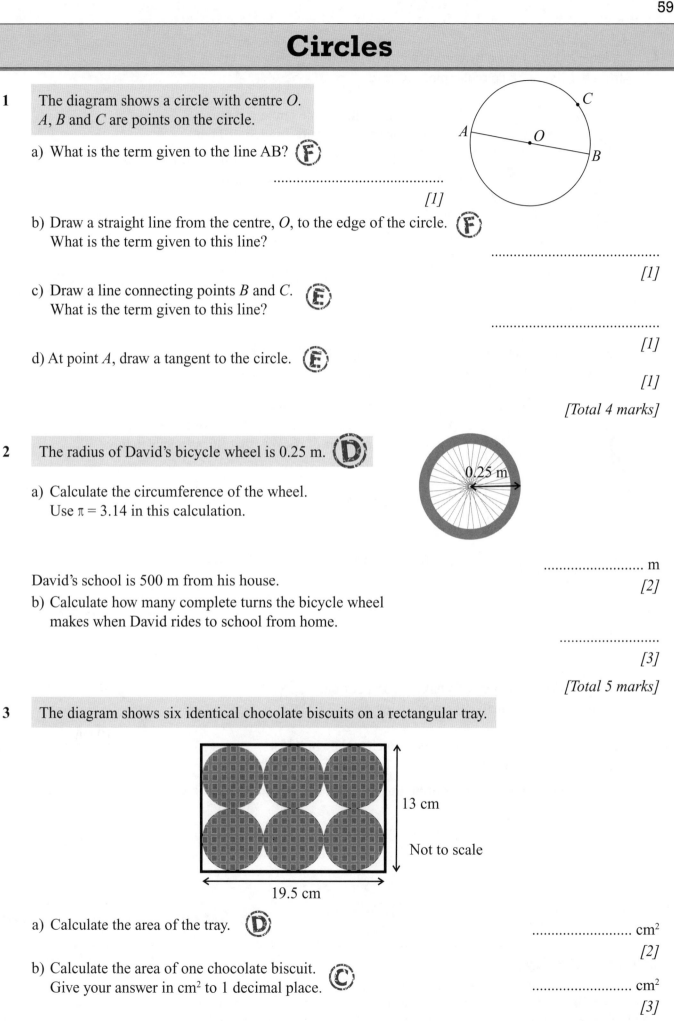

a) What is the term given to the line AB? (F)

....
[1]

b) Draw a straight line from the centre, O, to the edge of the circle. (F)
What is the term given to this line?

....
[1]

c) Draw a line connecting points B and C. (E)
What is the term given to this line?

....
[1]

d) At point A, draw a tangent to the circle. (E)

[1]

[Total 4 marks]

2 The radius of David's bicycle wheel is 0.25 m. (D)

a) Calculate the circumference of the wheel.
Use $\pi = 3.14$ in this calculation.

.... m
[2]

David's school is 500 m from his house.

b) Calculate how many complete turns the bicycle wheel
makes when David rides to school from home.

....
[3]

[Total 5 marks]

3 The diagram shows six identical chocolate biscuits on a rectangular tray.

13 cm

Not to scale

19.5 cm

a) Calculate the area of the tray. (D)

.... cm²
[2]

b) Calculate the area of one chocolate biscuit. (C)
Give your answer in cm² to 1 decimal place.

.... cm²
[3]

[Total 5 marks]

4 A letter "O" is formed by cutting a circular section from the centre of a circular piece of card. Ⓒ

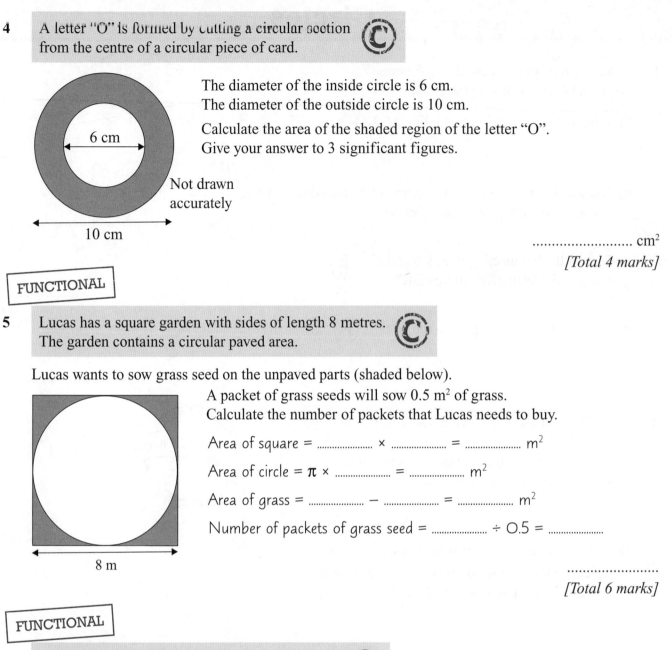

The diameter of the inside circle is 6 cm.
The diameter of the outside circle is 10 cm.

Calculate the area of the shaded region of the letter "O".
Give your answer to 3 significant figures.

6 cm

Not drawn accurately

10 cm

.... cm²

[Total 4 marks]

FUNCTIONAL

5 Lucas has a square garden with sides of length 8 metres. Ⓒ
The garden contains a circular paved area.

Lucas wants to sow grass seed on the unpaved parts (shaded below).

A packet of grass seeds will sow 0.5 m² of grass.
Calculate the number of packets that Lucas needs to buy.

Area of square = ... × .... = ... m²

Area of circle = π × .... = ... m²

Area of grass = ... − .... = ... m²

Number of packets of grass seed = ... ÷ 0.5 = ...

8 m

....

[Total 6 marks]

FUNCTIONAL

6 Zara is making cookies for a baking competition. Ⓒ
She makes them exactly 10 cm in diameter.

Zara wants to decorate the cookies with chocolate buttons.
She works out that there needs to be at least 3 cm² for each button.

What is the maximum number of buttons that she can put on each cookie?

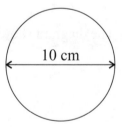

10 cm

....

[Total 5 marks]

Exam Practice Tip

Don't mix up radius and diameter — it seems obvious, but lots of people muddle them up in exams. The radius of a circle is half of its diameter. Think carefully about which one you're being given, and which one you need for a formula. You won't be given the formulas in the exam, so make sure you know them off by heart.

Score

29

Volume

1 The diagram below shows a prism made from centimetre cubes. **(F)**

Calculate the volume of the prism.

Don't forget the cubes you can't see.

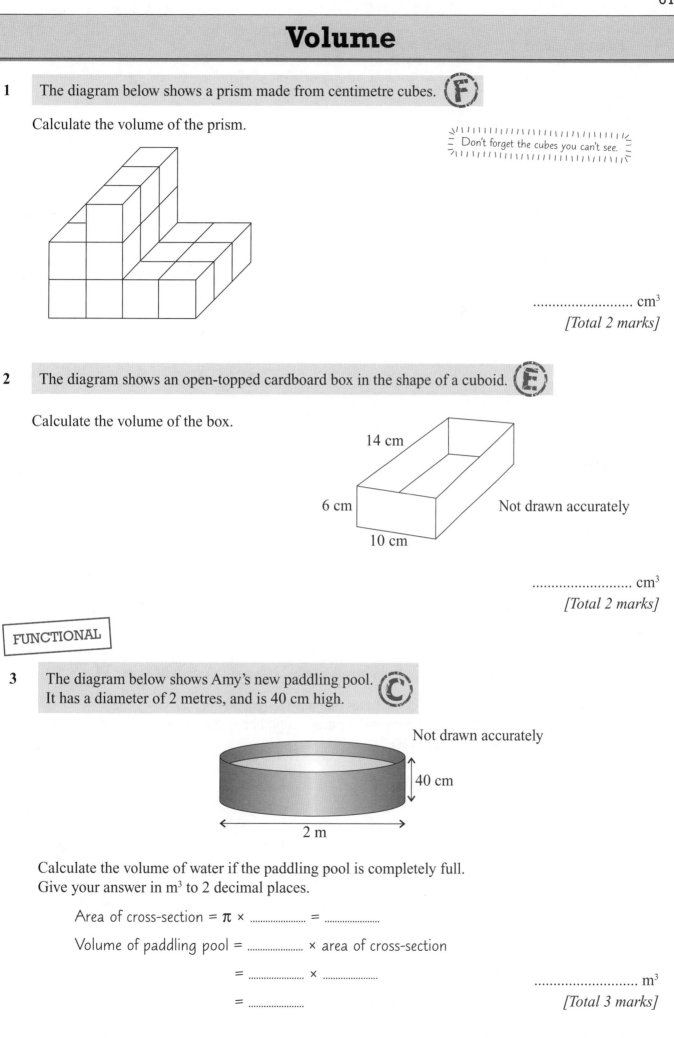

.... cm³

[Total 2 marks]

2 The diagram shows an open-topped cardboard box in the shape of a cuboid. **(E)**

Calculate the volume of the box.

14 cm

6 cm

10 cm

Not drawn accurately

.... cm³

[Total 2 marks]

FUNCTIONAL

3 The diagram below shows Amy's new paddling pool. **(C)**
It has a diameter of 2 metres, and is 40 cm high.

Not drawn accurately

40 cm

2 m

Calculate the volume of water if the paddling pool is completely full.
Give your answer in m³ to 2 decimal places.

Area of cross-section = π × .... = ...

Volume of paddling pool = ... × area of cross-section

= .... × ....

= ....

.... m³

[Total 3 marks]

4 Find the volume of the triangular prism shown below.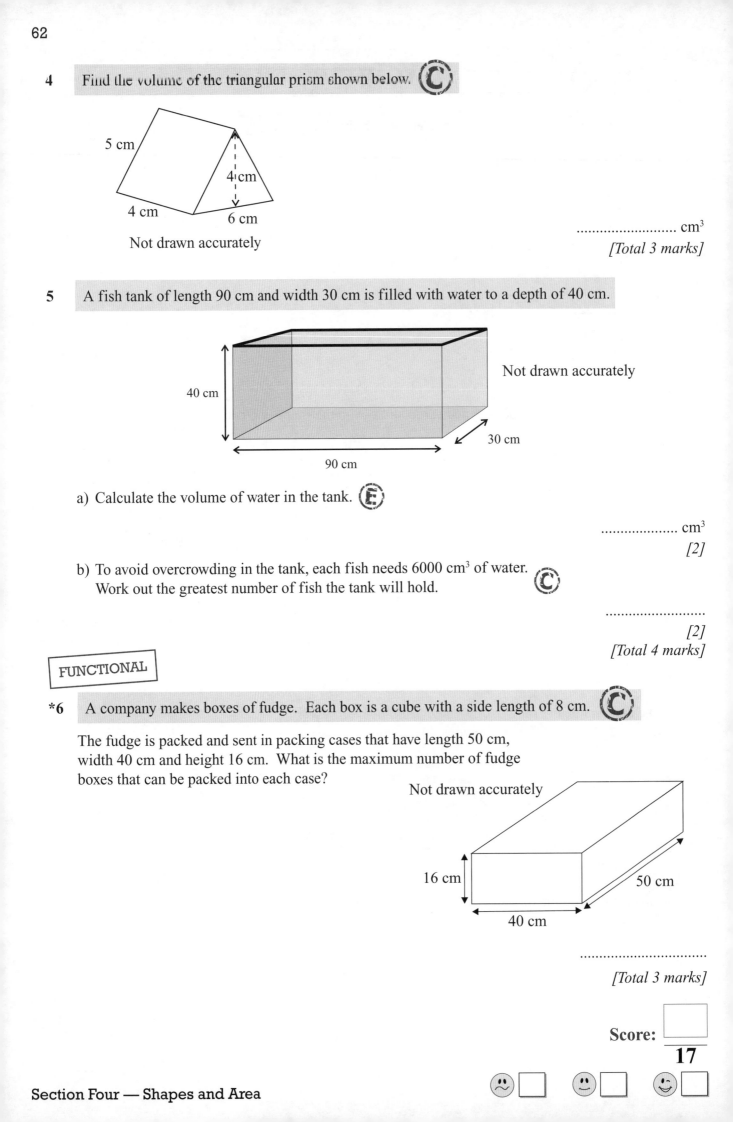

5 cm

4 cm

4 cm   6 cm

Not drawn accurately

.... cm³

[Total 3 marks]

5 A fish tank of length 90 cm and width 30 cm is filled with water to a depth of 40 cm.

Not drawn accurately

40 cm

30 cm

90 cm

a) Calculate the volume of water in the tank.

.... cm³

[2]

b) To avoid overcrowding in the tank, each fish needs 6000 cm³ of water.
   Work out the greatest number of fish the tank will hold.

....

[2]

[Total 4 marks]

FUNCTIONAL

*6 A company makes boxes of fudge. Each box is a cube with a side length of 8 cm.

The fudge is packed and sent in packing cases that have length 50 cm,
width 40 cm and height 16 cm. What is the maximum number of fudge
boxes that can be packed into each case?

Not drawn accurately

16 cm   50 cm

40 cm

....

[Total 3 marks]

Score:

17

Nets and Surface Area

1   Complete the net of the cuboid below. (E)

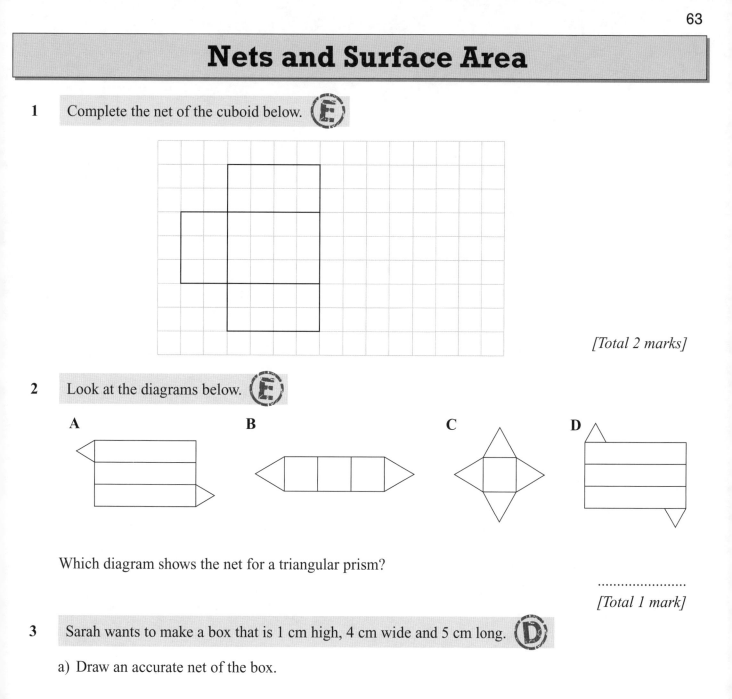

[Total 2 marks]

2   Look at the diagrams below. (E)

A   B   C   D

Which diagram shows the net for a triangular prism?

....

[Total 1 mark]

3   Sarah wants to make a box that is 1 cm high, 4 cm wide and 5 cm long. (D)

a) Draw an accurate net of the box.

[3]

b) Calculate the total area of card needed to make the box.
    Assume that no overlap is needed.

.... cm²

[3]

[Total 6 marks]

64

4 Here is a square-based pyramid. **(D)**

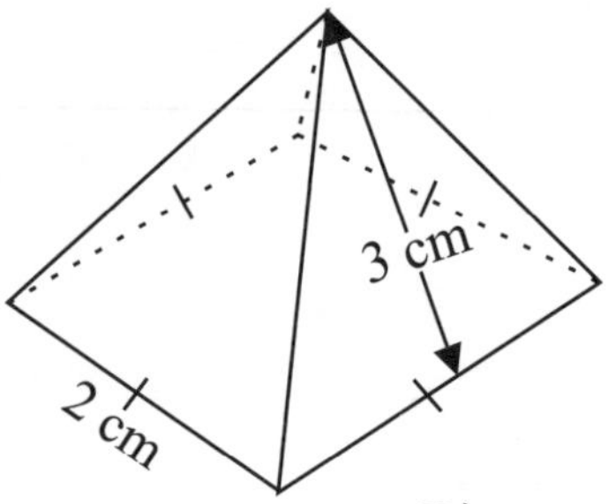

Diagram not
accurately drawn.

Draw an accurate net of the pyramid
on the centimetre grid on the right.

[Total 3 marks]

FUNCTIONAL

5 Dan has bought a new door for his garden shed. He needs to varnish the door all over **(C)** to make sure that it is weatherproof. The door is 2 m high, 1 m wide, and 3 cm thick.

One tin of varnish will cover 2.45 m² of wood, and Dan will need to give the door two coats of varnish. How many tins should he buy?

*Make sure you convert
all the measurements
into the same units.*

....

[Total 4 marks]

6 The diagram below shows a cylinder. **(C)**

Calculate the surface area of the cylinder. Give your answer in cm² to three significant figures.

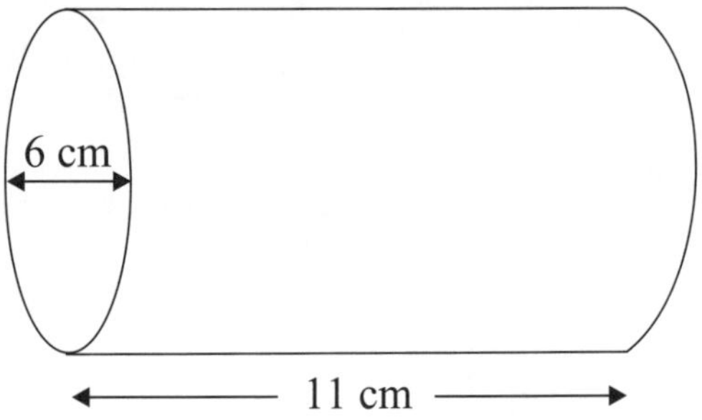

6 cm

11 cm

Diagram not
accurately drawn.

Area of cross-section = π × .... = ...

Circumference = π × .... = ...

Area of curved surface = circumference × length

= .... × .... = ...

Total surface area = (2 × ....) + ... = ...

.... cm²

[Total 4 marks]

Score:

20

Section Four — Shapes and Area

Measuring and Drawing Lines and Angles

1   *AB* is a straight line.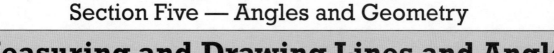

A ———————————————————————————— B

a) Measure the length of *AB*.

.... cm
[1]

b) Mark the midpoint of the line *AB* with a cross.

[1]

[Total 2 marks]

2   Triangle *ABC* is shown below.

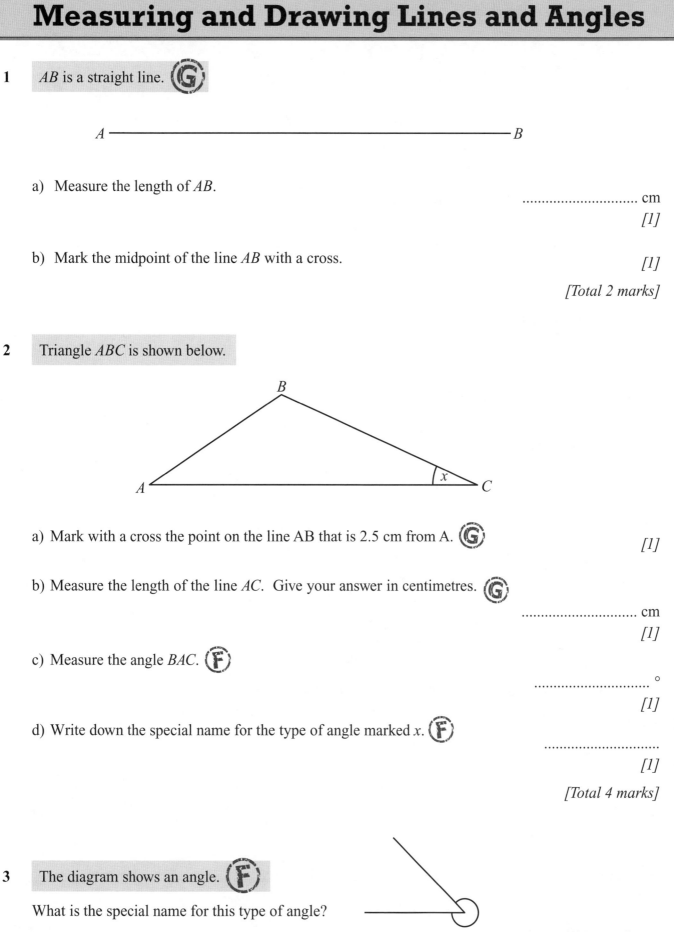

a) Mark with a cross the point on the line AB that is 2.5 cm from A.

[1]

b) Measure the length of the line *AC*. Give your answer in centimetres.

.... cm
[1]

c) Measure the angle *BAC*.

.... °
[1]

d) Write down the special name for the type of angle marked *x*.

....
[1]

[Total 4 marks]

3   The diagram shows an angle.

What is the special name for this type of angle?

....
[Total 1 mark]

4   The diagram below shows a quadrilateral.

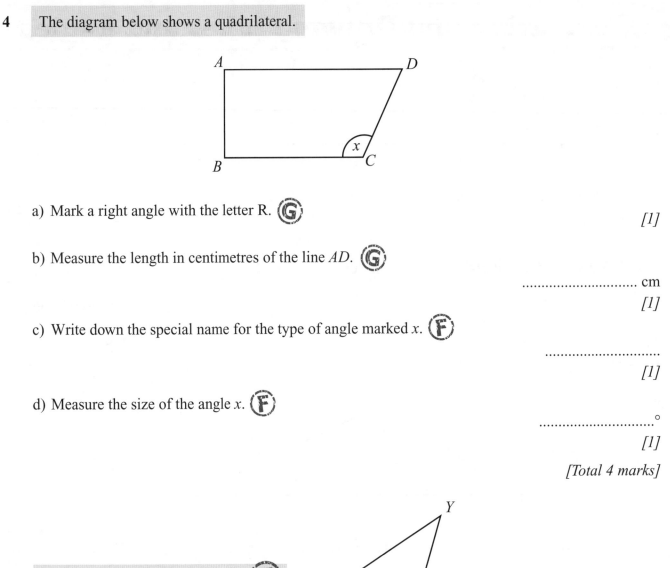

a) Mark a right angle with the letter R. (G)

[1]

b) Measure the length in centimetres of the line *AD*. (G)

.... cm

[1]

c) Write down the special name for the type of angle marked *x*. (F)

....

[1]

d) Measure the size of the angle *x*. (F)

............................°

[1]

[Total 4 marks]

5   Here is a sketch of triangle *XYZ*. (F)

Draw an accurate diagram of triangle *XYZ* in the space below.

[Total 3 marks]

Exam Practice Tip

Measuring and drawing lines and angles is all about taking your time and being careful — exciting stuff.
Make sure you've lined the ruler or the protractor up properly and double-check you're reading the right scale.
And finally, if you're measuring in mm or degrees, round to the nearest marking if there isn't one that's bang on.

Score

14

Five Angle Rules

1 Work out the size of the angle marked x.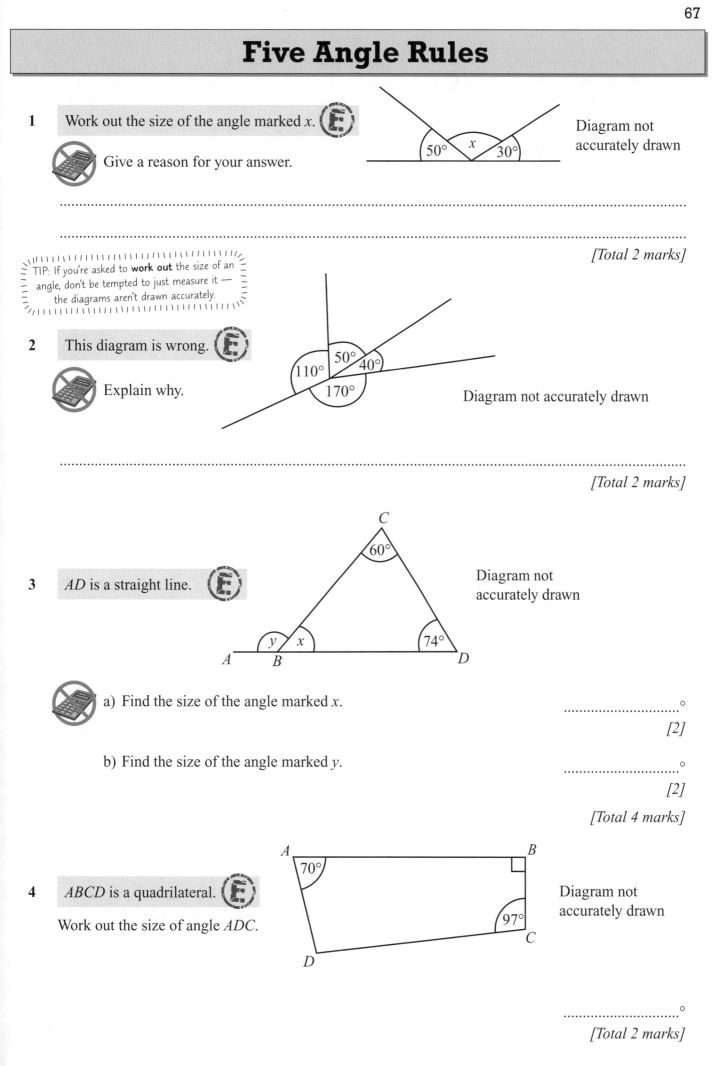

Give a reason for your answer.

Diagram not accurately drawn

$50°$ x $30°$

....

....

[Total 2 marks]

TIP: If you're asked to **work out** the size of an angle, don't be tempted to just measure it — the diagrams aren't drawn accurately.

2 This diagram is wrong.

Explain why.

$110°$ $50°$ $40°$ $170°$

Diagram not accurately drawn

....

[Total 2 marks]

3 AD is a straight line.

C

$60°$

y x $74°$

A B D

Diagram not accurately drawn

a) Find the size of the angle marked x.

........................°

[2]

b) Find the size of the angle marked y.

........................°

[2]

[Total 4 marks]

4 $ABCD$ is a quadrilateral.

Work out the size of angle ADC.

A $70°$ B

$97°$ C

D

Diagram not accurately drawn

........................°

[Total 2 marks]

Section Five — Angles and Geometry

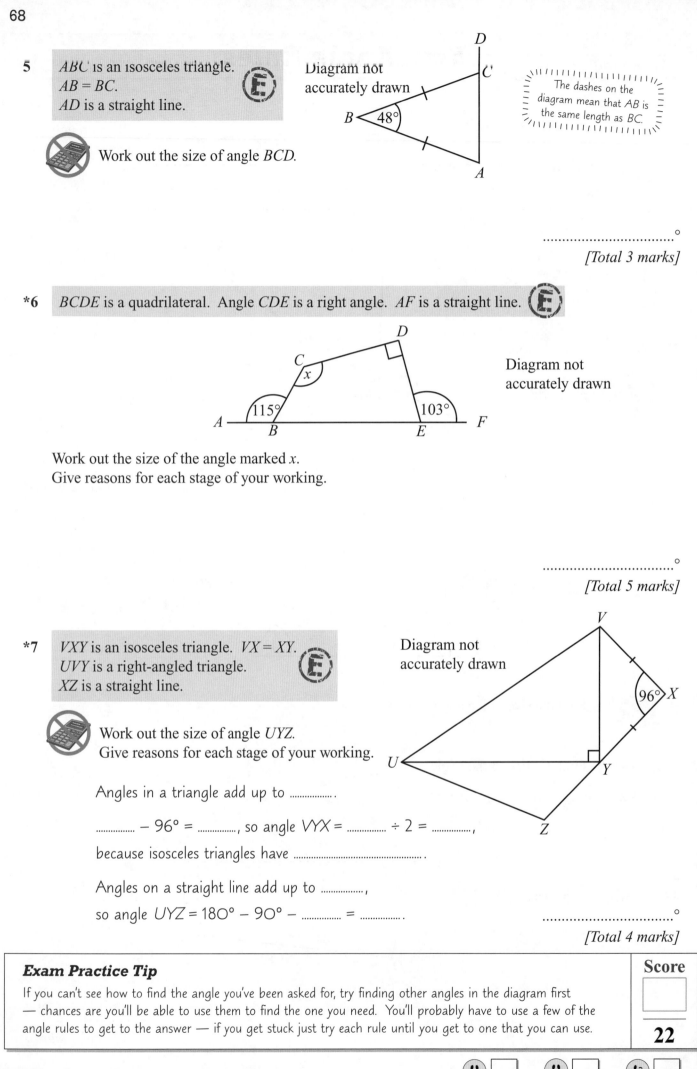

5 *ABC* is an isosceles triangle.
AB = *BC*.
AD is a straight line.

> The dashes on the diagram mean that *AB* is the same length as *BC*.

Diagram not accurately drawn

Work out the size of angle *BCD*.

...................................°

[Total 3 marks]

*6 *BCDE* is a quadrilateral. Angle *CDE* is a right angle. *AF* is a straight line.

Diagram not accurately drawn

Work out the size of the angle marked *x*.
Give reasons for each stage of your working.

...................................°

[Total 5 marks]

*7 *VXY* is an isosceles triangle. *VX* = *XY*.
UVY is a right-angled triangle.
XZ is a straight line.

Diagram not accurately drawn

Work out the size of angle *UYZ*.
Give reasons for each stage of your working.

Angles in a triangle add up to ....

.... − 96° = ... , so angle *VYX* = ... ÷ 2 = ... ,

because isosceles triangles have ....

Angles on a straight line add up to .... ,

so angle *UYZ* = 180° − 90° − .... = ...

...................................°

[Total 4 marks]

Exam Practice Tip

If you can't see how to find the angle you've been asked for, try finding other angles in the diagram first — chances are you'll be able to use them to find the one you need. You'll probably have to use a few of the angle rules to get to the answer — if you get stuck just try each rule until you get to one that you can use.

Score

22

Parallel Lines

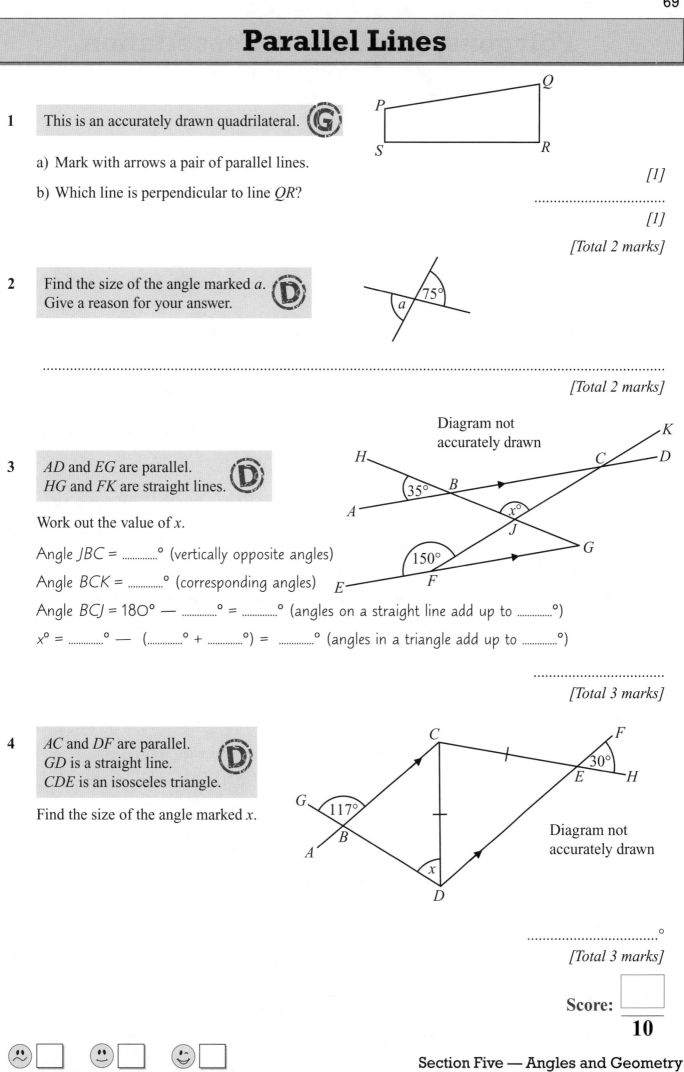

1 This is an accurately drawn quadrilateral. **G**

 a) Mark with arrows a pair of parallel lines.

 [1]

 b) Which line is perpendicular to line *QR*?

 ....

 [1]

 [Total 2 marks]

2 Find the size of the angle marked *a*. **D**
 Give a reason for your answer.

 ....

 [Total 2 marks]

3 *AD* and *EG* are parallel. **D**
 HG and *FK* are straight lines.

 Diagram not accurately drawn

 Work out the value of *x*.

 Angle *JBC* = ...° (vertically opposite angles)

 Angle *BCK* = ...° (corresponding angles)

 Angle *BCJ* = 180° — ....° = ...° (angles on a straight line add up to ....°)

 $x°$ = ...° — (..............° + ...°) = ...° (angles in a triangle add up to ....°)

 ....

 [Total 3 marks]

4 *AC* and *DF* are parallel. **D**
 GD is a straight line.
 CDE is an isosceles triangle.

 Find the size of the angle marked *x*.

 Diagram not accurately drawn

 ....°

 [Total 3 marks]

 Score:

 10

70

Polygons, Angles and Tessellation

1   Answer the questions below.

   a) How many sides does a heptagon have?

                                         ....

                                              [1]

   b) What is the name of the shape below?

                            ....

                                             [1]

                                   [Total 2 marks]

2   The diagram shows a regular pentagon and an equilateral triangle.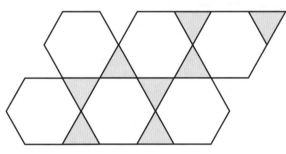

      Work out the size of the angle *p*.

Diagram not accurately drawn

                               ....°

                                   [Total 4 marks]

3   Kate's kitchen is tiled with regular hexagons and equilateral triangles.

   a) Work out the interior angle of a regular hexagon.

      Exterior angle = 360° ÷ ....

                  = ...

      Interior angle = 180° — .... = ...°

                                             [2]

  *b) Explain why regular hexagons and equilateral triangles can fit together with no gaps.

      Each angle in an equilateral triangle is 60°. The interior angle of a regular hexagon is   °.

      Angles round a point add up to   °.

      60° +   ° +   ° +   ° =   °, so 2 regular hexagons and 2 equilateral triangles

      can meet at a point.

                                               [3]

                                   [Total 5 marks]

Exam Practice Tip

Don't panic if you get an 'Explain why...' question on polygons — all you're being asked to do is use the rules you know about angles. If you just remember that the exterior angles of a polygon add up to 360°, angles on a line add up to 180° and angles round a point add up to 360°, you should be fine.

Score

11

Section Five — Angles and Geometry

Transformations

1   Reflect the shaded shape in the mirror line.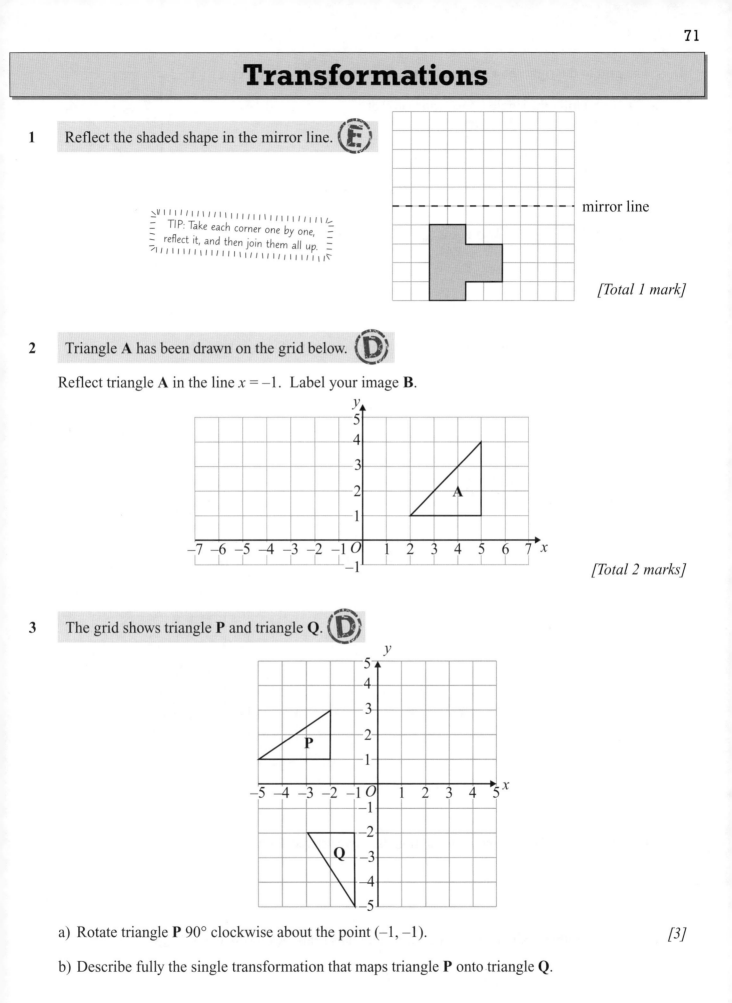

TIP: Take each corner one by one, reflect it, and then join them all up.

mirror line

[Total 1 mark]

2   Triangle **A** has been drawn on the grid below.

Reflect triangle **A** in the line $x = -1$. Label your image **B**.

[Total 2 marks]

3   The grid shows triangle **P** and triangle **Q**.

a) Rotate triangle **P** 90° clockwise about the point (–1, –1).   *[3]*

b) Describe fully the single transformation that maps triangle **P** onto triangle **Q**.

....

[3]

[Total 6 marks]

Section Five — Angles and Geometry

4 The grid to the right shows shape **A** and shape **B**. **(D)**

a) Describe fully the single transformation that maps shape **A** onto shape **B**.

....

....

[2]

b) Reflect shape **A** in the line $y = x$. Label the image **C**.

[2]

c) Describe fully the single transformation that maps shape **C** onto shape **B**.

....

[3]

[Total 7 marks]

5 Shape **R**, shape **S** and shape **T** have been drawn on the grid to the right.

a) Translate shape **T** by the vector $\begin{pmatrix} -1 \\ 3 \end{pmatrix}$. **(D)** [1]

b) Describe fully the single transformation that maps shape **T** onto shape **R**. **(D)**

....

[2]

c) Describe fully the single transformation that maps shape **R** onto shape **S**. **(C)**

....

....

[3]

[Total 6 marks]

Section Five — Angles and Geometry

6   On the grid enlarge the triangle by a scale factor of 3, centre (–4, 0). **C**

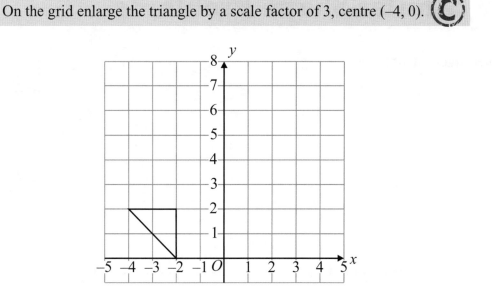

[Total 3 marks]

7   Shape **A** has been drawn on the grid. **C**

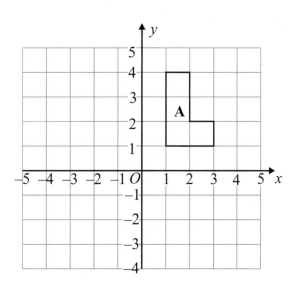

Shape **A** is reflected in the *x*-axis to give shape **B**.
Shape **B** is rotated 180° about the origin to give shape **C**.

Describe fully the single transformation which maps shape **A** onto shape **C**.

....

[Total 4 marks]

Exam Practice Tip

Make sure you give all the details when you describe a transformation — if a question is worth three marks then you'll probably need to give three bits of information. For example, for enlargements give the scale factor and the centre of enlargement, and for rotations give the centre, the direction and the angle of rotation.

Score

29

Similar Shape Problems

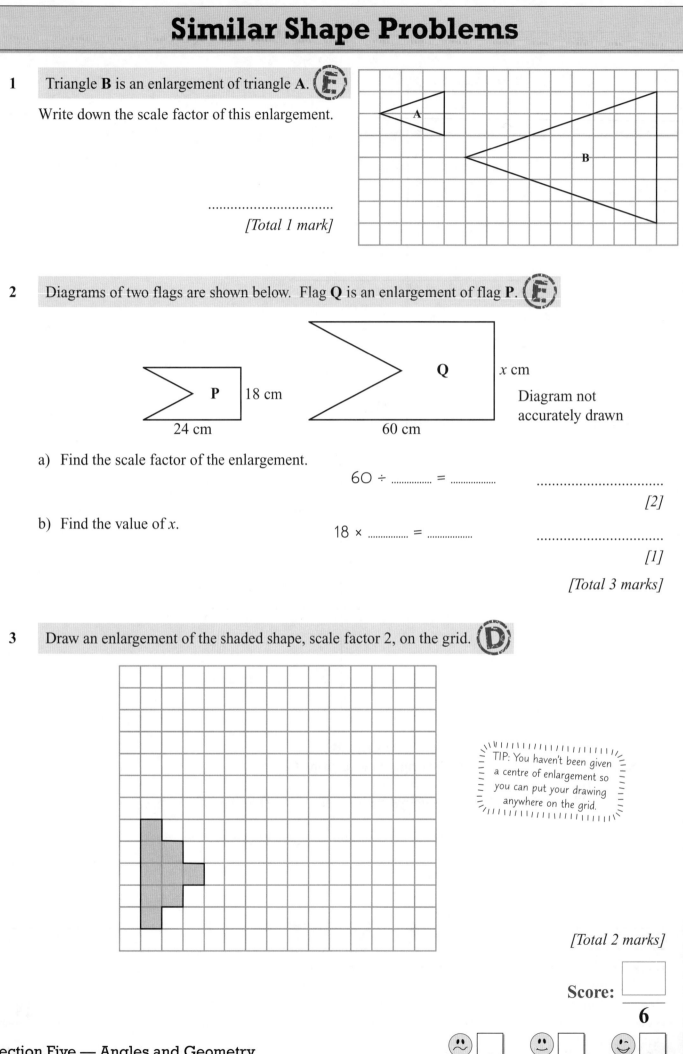

1   Triangle **B** is an enlargement of triangle **A**. Ⓔ

Write down the scale factor of this enlargement.

....

[Total 1 mark]

2   Diagrams of two flags are shown below. Flag **Q** is an enlargement of flag **P**. Ⓔ

P | 18 cm

24 cm

Q | *x* cm

Diagram not
accurately drawn

60 cm

a) Find the scale factor of the enlargement.

60 ÷ .... = ...

[2]

b) Find the value of *x*.

18 × .... = ...

[1]

[Total 3 marks]

3   Draw an enlargement of the shaded shape, scale factor 2, on the grid. Ⓓ

TIP: You haven't been given
a centre of enlargement so
you can put your drawing
anywhere on the grid.

[Total 2 marks]

Score:

6

Section Five — Angles and Geometry

Triangle Construction

1   Side *BC* of the equilateral triangle *ABC* has been accurately drawn below.

B ─────────────────────────── C

a) Use a ruler and compasses to complete the accurate drawing of triangle *ABC*. (E)   [1]

b) Construct the bisector of angle *ACB* of the triangle. (C)   [2]
   You must show all your construction lines.

[Total 3 marks]

2   The diagram below is a sketch of triangle *ABC*. (E)

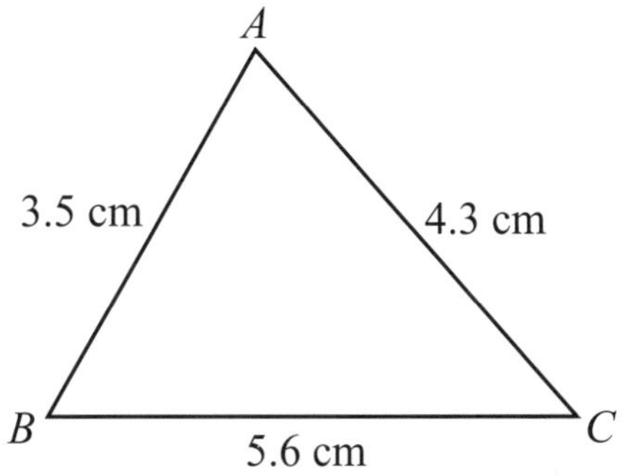

3.5 cm   4.3 cm

Diagram not
accurately drawn

B   5.6 cm   C

Use a ruler and compasses to make an accurate drawing of triangle *ABC* in the space below.
You must show all your construction lines.

[Total 3 marks]

Score: ☐

6

Loci and Constructions

1   Accurately draw a circle of diameter 4 cm. (F)

Use the point *A* as the centre of your circle.

A •

[Total 2 marks]

2   Two sides of quadrilateral *PQRS* have been accurately drawn below.
The other two sides are side *PS* and side *RS*. Side *PS* is 4.2 cm and side *RS* is 6.7 cm.

You must show all your construction lines.

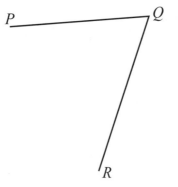

a) Use a ruler and compasses to accurately complete the quadrilateral. (E)   *[2]*

b) Construct the perpendicular to the line segment *PQ* that passes through point *R*. (C)   *[2]*

[Total 4 marks]

3   Salman has a robot which can walk a maximum of 10 m from the beam *AB*. (C)

Shade the region on the diagram where Salman's robot can walk, using the scale shown.

A ———————————— *B*

Scale: 1 cm represents 5 m

[Total 2 marks]

4   A town council wants to put up a new visitor information board. They think that it should be placed closer to the park than to the library, but also closer to the station than to the park.

The diagram below shows a scale map of the town centre.
Shade in the region of the town where the board could be placed.

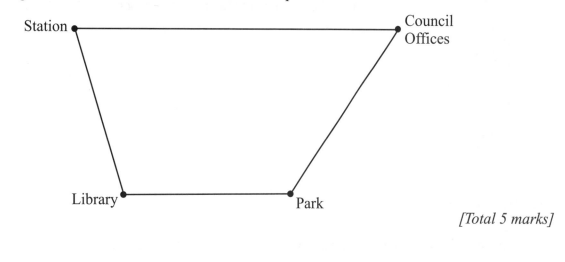

[Total 5 marks]

5   Hilary and Tony are deciding where they would like to put a pond in their garden.
Hilary wants the centre of the pond to be 1 m from the garden wall *BC*.
Tony wants the centre of the pond to be 2 m from the tree *F*.

Accurately complete the plan of the garden below by using a cross (✕) to mark any points where Hilary and Tony would both be happy for the centre of the pond to be.

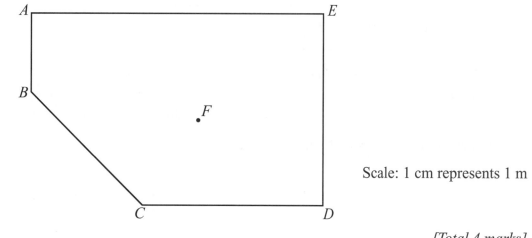

Scale: 1 cm represents 1 m

[Total 4 marks]

Exam Practice Tip

You won't always be told that you need to use a ruler and compasses, but if you're asked to <u>construct</u> something then you'll be expected to use them. Make sure you don't rub out your construction lines — even if it doesn't ask for them in the question you won't get all the marks unless you show how you did your construction.

Score

17

Section Five — Angles and Geometry

Pythagoras' Theorem

1 A 3.5 m long ladder is resting against a vertical wall and on the horizontal ground. For safety the bottom of the ladder must be at least 2.1 m away from the wall.

How far up the wall can the ladder safely reach?

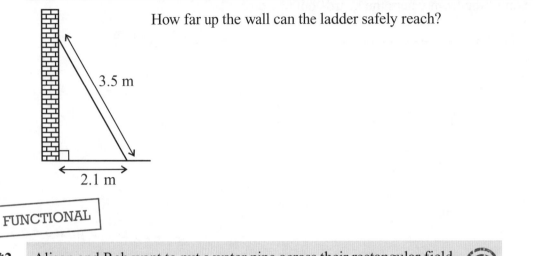

3.5 m

2.1 m

.... m
[Total 3 marks]

FUNCTIONAL

*2 Alison and Rob want to put a water pipe across their rectangular field. The diagram below shows their field.

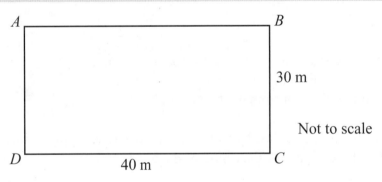

A   *B*

30 m

D   40 m   *C*

Not to scale

> TIP: Draw a quick sketch using the information that you're given in the question — then you can easily see where to put the numbers in the Pythagoras formula.

The pipe must run from a tap at point *A* to the shed at point *C*.

Alison wants to put the pipe across the diagonal of the field.
Rob wants to put the pipe round the edge of the field.

The pipe costs £8.35 per metre.

If they put the pipe across the diagonal they will have to dig a trench and replace the grass, which will cost £202.50. If they put the pipe round the edge they will not have to dig a trench.

Which option is cheaper? Explain your answer.

....

....

[Total 6 marks]

Exam Practice Tip	**Score**
You probably won't be <u>told</u> to use Pythagoras' theorem in the question — you'll have to remember it's something you can use if you've got two sides of a right-angled triangle and you're looking for the third side. If you get a wordy question it's a good idea to sketch a diagram to make sure your sides are in the right place.	**9**

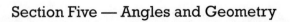

Units and Conversions

1   The table below shows different units of measurements.

a) Complete the table using the most appropriate unit of measurement. (F)

	Imperial	**Metric**
Length of a skirt	inches	....
Weight of a rabbit	....	kilograms
Volume of a milk jug	pints	....

[3]

b) The length of a classroom is 887 cm. How long is that in metres? (E)

.... m

[1]

c) A bunch of bananas weighs 1.3 kg. How much is this in grams? (E)

.... g

[1]

[Total 5 marks]

FUNCTIONAL

2   Emma is having a party with some friends. (E)

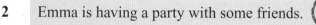

She has 2.5 litres of orange juice.
How many 250 ml cups can be filled from it?

.... cups

[Total 3 marks]

FUNCTIONAL

3   Nicole wants to post some books to a friend in another country.
Each book weighs 1.5 lb and each package can hold a maximum weight of 2500 g. (E)

How many books can she send in one package?

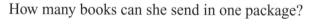

Hint — you need to do a conversion
between kilograms and pounds.

....

[Total 4 marks]

4 The formula to convert kilometres (k) to miles (m) is $m = \dfrac{5k}{8}$.

a) How many miles is 40 km? **E**

.... miles

[2]

b) A giraffe can run at 60 km/h.
Show that a giraffe could be outrun by a camel running at 40 mph. **D**

....

....

[2]

FUNCTIONAL

[Total 4 marks]

5 1 litre = $1\dfrac{3}{4}$ pints. **D**

You could start by converting 14 pints into litres.

Margaret needs 14 pints of water to fill up her fish tank.
She uses three different sized containers to fill up the tank.
One container holds 520 ml, one holds 540 ml and the other holds 720 ml.

To fill up the tank, Margaret uses the 720 ml container three times,
the 520 ml container five times and then the 540 ml container to finish filling it up.

How many times must she fill up the 540 ml container to finish filling the fish tank?

....

[Total 5 marks]

6 The playing surface of a snooker table has an area of 39 200 cm². **D**

Convert the area of the snooker table into m².

.... m²

[Total 2 marks]

Exam Practice Tip

Make sure you learn the rough conversions between metric units (kg, km, cm and litres) and imperial units (pounds, miles, feet, gallons and pints). I know it's dull just memorising numbers, but you might not be given them in the exam. You also need to know metric-to-metric conversions, but thankfully those are MUCH easier.

Score

23

Reading Scales

1   Give the readings from each of the scales below.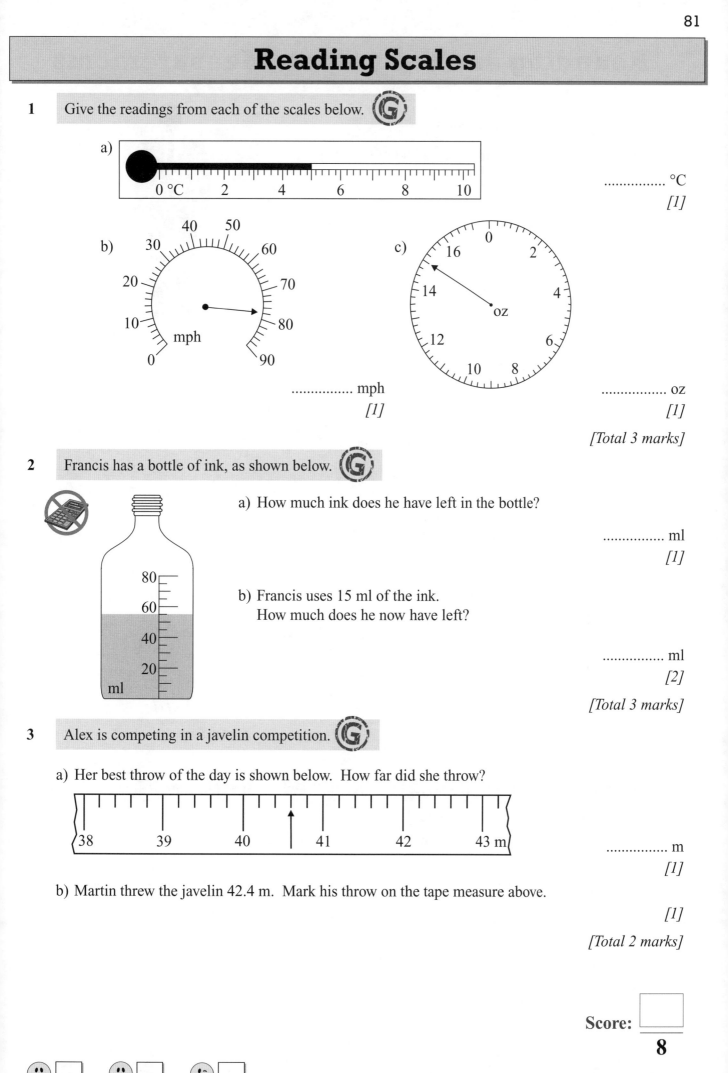

a)

.... °C
[1]

b)

.... mph
[1]

c)

.... oz
[1]

[Total 3 marks]

2   Francis has a bottle of ink, as shown below.

a) How much ink does he have left in the bottle?

.... ml
[1]

b) Francis uses 15 ml of the ink.
   How much does he now have left?

.... ml
[2]

[Total 3 marks]

3   Alex is competing in a javelin competition.

a) Her best throw of the day is shown below. How far did she throw?

.... m
[1]

b) Martin threw the javelin 42.4 m. Mark his throw on the tape measure above.

[1]

[Total 2 marks]

Score:

8

Rounding and Estimating Measurements

1 The man in this picture is of average height. (F)

Use this information to estimate the height of the penguin.

.... cm

[Total 3 marks]

2 Mandy uses a thermometer to measure the temperature outside.

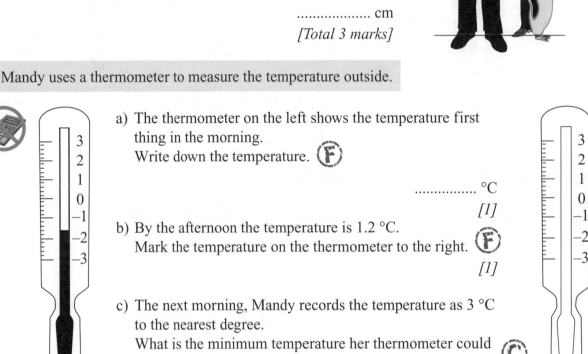

a) The thermometer on the left shows the temperature first
thing in the morning.
Write down the temperature. (F)

.... °C
[1]

b) By the afternoon the temperature is 1.2 °C.
Mark the temperature on the thermometer to the right. (F)
[1]

c) The next morning, Mandy records the temperature as 3 °C
to the nearest degree. (C)
What is the minimum temperature her thermometer could
show in order for her to record this temperature?

.... °C
[1]

[Total 3 marks]

3 Joseph is weighing himself. His scales give his weight to the nearest kilogram. (C)

According to his scales, Joseph is 57 kg.
What are the minimum and maximum weights that he could be?

Minimum weight: .... kg

Maximum weight: .... kg

[Total 2 marks]

Score:

8

Section Six — Measures

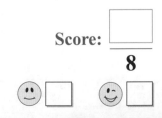

Reading Timetables

1 A teacher set her students a test to do before lunchtime. (F)

a) The clock shows the time when the students started the test.
What time is shown on the clock?

....

[1]

b) The test took the students one hour and twenty minutes to complete.
Show what time they finished on this clock.

[1]

[Total 2 marks]

2 A cake has to be baked for 2¼ hours. Mary puts the cake in the oven at 9:55 am. (F)

What time should Mary take the cake out of the oven?

....

[Total 2 marks]

3 Part of the bus timetable from Coventry to Rugby is shown below.

Coventry	1445	1615	1745
Bubbenhall	–	1640	1810
Stretton	1514	1654	1824
Birdingbury	–	1704	–
Rugby	1535	1730	1840

The dashes on the timetable mean the bus doesn't stop.

a) What time does the 1615 bus from Coventry leave Birdingbury? (F)

....

[1]

b) Lisa arrives at Birdingbury bus stop at 1658. (F)
How long will she have to wait for the bus to Rugby?

.... minutes

[1]

The 1615 bus from Coventry continues to Lutterworth after Rugby. It arrives in Lutterworth at 1815.

c) Anne lives in Bubbenhall. If she catches this bus from her home, (E)
how long will it take her to get to Lutterworth?

.... h .... mins

[2]

[Total 4 marks]

4 Deirdre is planning a train journey.

a) It will take 25 minutes to get to the station and she wants to be there at 11 15.
What is the latest time she should leave home?

....

[2]

b) The train leaves at 11 35 and arrives at 13 22.
How long is the journey? Give your answer in minutes.

.... minutes

[2]

[Total 4 marks]

5 Sorcha is getting ready to go on holiday. (E)

She has to leave the house at 09 55. Before she goes on holiday, Sorcha must do the following:

Task	Time (mins)
pack bag	20
iron clothes	15
water plants	10

What time must she start getting ready for her holiday?

....

[Total 3 marks]

6 Isaac and Ultan are making a model robot. (E)

They took 20 minutes to read the instructions and then 10 minutes to build each section of the robot.
The robot has 14 sections. They started reading the instructions at 14 55.
What time did they finish building the robot?

20 minutes + (............. × ....) = ... minutes in total

= .... minutes ÷ .... = ... hours .... minutes

Time finished = ... + ... hours .... minutes

= ....

....

[Total 4 marks]

Score:

19

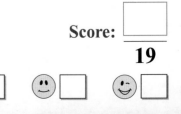

Compass Directions and Bearings

1   This is a plan of an adventure park. (F)

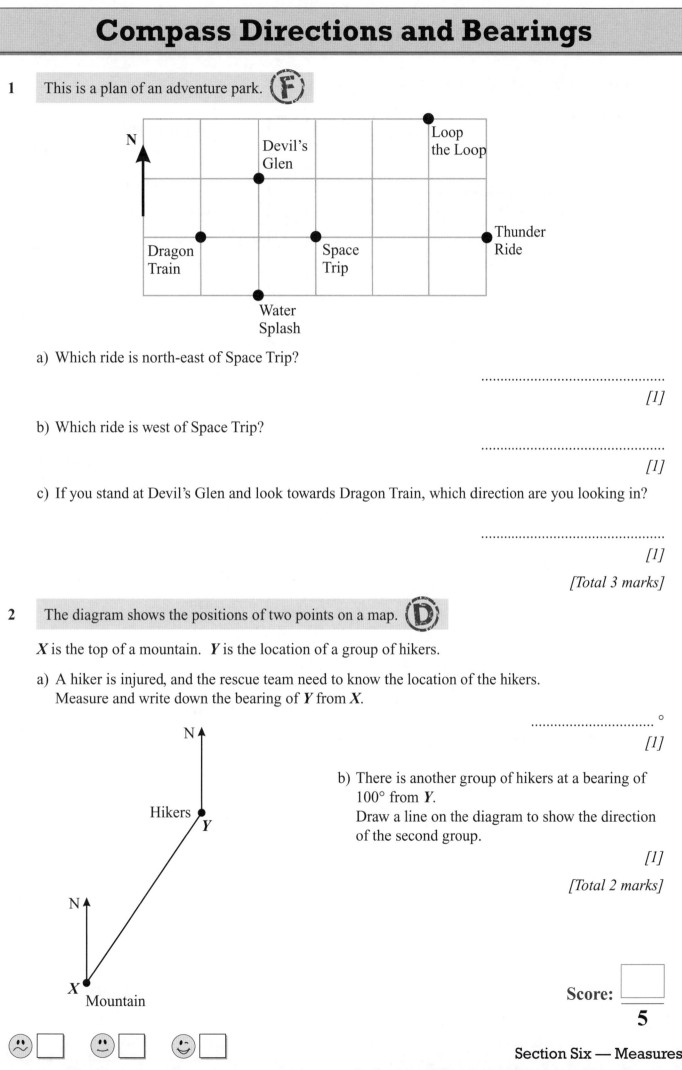

a) Which ride is north-east of Space Trip?

....

[1]

b) Which ride is west of Space Trip?

....

[1]

c) If you stand at Devil's Glen and look towards Dragon Train, which direction are you looking in?

....

[1]

[Total 3 marks]

2   The diagram shows the positions of two points on a map. (D)

X is the top of a mountain. Y is the location of a group of hikers.

a) A hiker is injured, and the rescue team need to know the location of the hikers.
   Measure and write down the bearing of Y from X.

..............................°

[1]

b) There is another group of hikers at a bearing of
   100° from Y.
   Draw a line on the diagram to show the direction
   of the second group.

[1]

[Total 2 marks]

Score: ☐

5

Maps and Scale Drawings

1   Douglas drew a scale drawing of his dining room. (E)

						Cupboard		
								Shelves
		Dining table						

a) His dining table is 2 m long.
   What is the scale of this drawing?

      1 cm to .... m

[1]

b) Work out the real distance from
   the dining table to the shelves.

      .... m

[1]

c) What is the real area of the dining room?

      .... m²

[3]

[Total 5 marks]

2   This map is drawn to a scale of 1 cm to 2 km. (E)

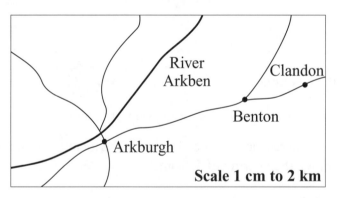

River
Arkben

Clandon

Benton

Arkburgh

Scale 1 cm to 2 km

a) Work out the actual distance between Arkburgh and Benton.

      .... km

[1]

b) Madeline cycles 7 km to school. How far would this be on the map?

      .... cm

[1]

[Total 2 marks]

Score: ☐

7

Section Six — Measures

Speed

1   John and Alan hired a van. Their receipt gave them information about how much time they spent travelling in the van, and how fast they went.

> Travelling time: 1 hour 15 minutes
> Average Speed: 56 km/h

Calculate the distance that John and Alan travelled in the van.

.... km

[Total 2 marks]

2   Beatrix is on a cycling holiday in Cumbria.
The table below shows the distances between each of the places she visits.

Keswick		
26 miles	**Windermere**	
33 miles	5 miles	**Hawkshead**

On Friday it took her 45 minutes to cycle from Hawkshead to Windermere.

On Saturday, she then cycled from Windermere, arriving in Keswick $3\frac{1}{4}$ hours later.

On Sunday, she cycled back from Keswick to Hawkshead in 3 hours 45 minutes.

*a) On which day did Beatrix ride her bike at the fastest average speed?

....

[4]

b) Work out Beatrix's average cycling speed over all three days. Give your answer to 1 decimal place.

Overall speed = $\dfrac{\text{............................}}{\text{...................}}$

$= \dfrac{\text{............} + \text{............} + \text{............}}{\text{............} + \text{............} + \text{............}} = \dfrac{\text{..............}}{\text{..............}} = \text{................}$ mph

.... mph

[3]

[Total 7 marks]

Score:

9

Collecting Data

1   Leah is doing a questionnaire at her school to find out how popular after-school activities are. **C**

Your response boxes should allow for all possible answers to the question.

a) Design a question for Leah to include in her questionnaire. You should include suitable response boxes.

[2]

Leah asks pupils at an after-school drama club to complete her questionnaire.

b) Write down **one** reason why this might not be a suitable sample.

....

....

[1]

[Total 3 marks]

2   Mike wants to find out how often people in his year group go to watch football matches. **C**

He includes the question below in a survey.

| How often do you go to watch football matches? |
| Sometimes   A lot |
| □   □ |

a) Give **one** thing that is wrong with this question.

....

....

[1]

Mike decides to ask the boys in his football team to do his survey.

b) Give one reason why this sample may not give him reliable information.

....

....

[1]

There are 100 people in Mike's year group.

c) Describe a method he could use to take a simple random sample of these people.

....

....

[2]

[Total 4 marks]

3 Faye wants to find out how often teenagers buy chocolate bars. ©

She writes the following question to ask in a survey.

> How many chocolate bars have you bought?
>
> 1 – 2   2 – 3   3 – 4
>
> ☐   ☐   ☐

Write two things that are wrong with the question above.

1. ....

2. ....

[Total 2 marks]

4 Jane wants to find out how often people are visiting the leisure centre.

a) Design a suitable data collection sheet she could use to record this information. Ⓓ

[3]

Jane wants to improve membership numbers. She designs a questionnaire.
Here is one of her questions:

> Do you agree the facilities need improving?

b) Give one reason why this is not a good question. ©

....

[1]

c) Rewrite the question so that it is more suitable. ©

[2]

Jane stands in the entrance of the leisure centre to ask people her questionnaire. ©
d) Explain why this is not a good way of getting information to improve membership.

....

....

[1]

[Total 7 marks]

Exam Practice Tip

In the exam, you might be asked to say why a particular survey question isn't very good. Always look at two things — the way it's worded and whether the response boxes are suitable. You might also get asked why a particular sample isn't good. Bias is often the problem here — think about whether the sample is representative.

Score

16

Mean, Median, Mode and Range

1   One evening Preya makes 10 phone calls. When the bill comes it shows how long each call was, in minutes. The call lengths are listed below. (F)

     10   12   25   3   37   13   12   18   41   33

   a) Work out the median length of Preya's calls.

.... minutes
[2]

   b) Calculate the mean phone call length.
      Give your answer to the nearest minute.

.... minutes
[2]

   c) What is the range?

.... minutes
[2]

[Total 6 marks]

2   Company A employs 5 people.
   Their annual salaries are listed below.

     £18 000   £38 500   £18 000   £25 200   £18 000

   a) Write down the mode. (F)

£ ....
[1]

   b) What is the median annual salary? (F)

£ ....
[1]

Company B has a mean annual salary of £24 150.
   c) Compare the mean annual salary of Company A and Company B. (E)

....

....

[3]

[Total 5 marks]

3   Sam thinks of three different whole numbers. (F)

The numbers have a range of 6 and a mean of 4.
What are the three numbers?

.................., ..., ...
[Total 2 marks]

Exam Practice Tip

Remember — the mode is the most common value, the median is the middle value (when the data is written in order), the mean is the sum of all the values divided by the number of values, and the range is the highest value minus the lowest value. It's usually a good idea to write your data in ascending order before you do anything else.

Score

13

Tables

1   Ryan is looking at properties in a new development.
    The table below shows information on these properties.

Property name	House/apartment	No. of bedrooms	Size (square feet)	Price (£)
The Apricot	House	5	1136	319 995
The Ivy	Apartment	2	526	119 995
The Lavender	House	3	744	189 995
The Oak	House	4	892	244 995
The Willow	Apartment	3	608	144 995

a) Which property has the fewest bedrooms?

    ....

    [1]

b) How many of these properties are **houses** that are smaller than 1000 square feet?

    ....

    [1]

    [Total 2 marks]

FUNCTIONAL

*2   Mr and Mrs White and their three children want to go on holiday next year.
     They can go for a week in either June or July.
     The table below shows prices in £ per adult and per child for a week.

Departure Date	Adult	Child
01 Jan — 19 Mar	140	125
20 Mar — 21 May	180	150
22 May — 30 Jun	300	290
01 July — 8 Sep	330	275
9 Sep — 26 Nov	230	160
27 Nov — 31 Dec	270	210

Compare the cost of the White family going on holiday for a week in June with the cost
of a week in July.

....

....

....

....

....

[Total 4 marks]

Score:

6

Pictograms

1 This pictogram shows the number of jars of jam sold in a campsite shop in one month. (G)

a) How many jars of strawberry jam were sold?

....
[1]

Strawberry Jam	🍓 🍓 🍓 🍓
Blackberry Jam	🍓 🍓 🍓
Raspberry Jam	

🍓 Represents 10 jars

The shop sold 35 jars of raspberry jam.
b) Complete the pictogram. [1]

c) How many jars of jam were sold altogether by the shop?

....
[1]

[Total 3 marks]

2 This pictogram shows the number of eggs laid by some chickens (G) at a farm on Monday, Tuesday and Wednesday.

Monday	◯ ◯ ◯ ◔
Tuesday	◯ ◯ ◖
Wednesday	◯ ◯ ◯ ◯ ◯
Thursday	
Friday	

◯ = 8 eggs

Pay attention to the key, which shows how many things each symbol stands for.

a) How many eggs were laid on Monday?

....
[1]

b) How many more eggs were laid on Wednesday than Tuesday?

....
[1]

24 eggs were laid on Thursday.
18 eggs were laid on Friday.
c) Show this information on the pictogram. [2]

[Total 4 marks]

Score:

7

Bar Charts

1 The dual bar chart below shows the number of cups of tea and coffee sold in a cafe each day.

Number of cups (y-axis)

Legend: Tea (light), Coffee (dark)

Monday Tuesday Wednesday Thursday Friday

a) How many cups of tea were sold on Wednesday?

....

[1]

b) On which day did the cafe sell 15 more cups of coffee than tea?

....

[1]

On Friday, the cafe sold 45 cups of tea and 30 cups of coffee.
c) Show this information on the bar chart.

[2]

d) Over the 5 days, did the cafe sell more cups of tea or coffee?

....

[2]

[Total 6 marks]

2 This table shows some information about the favourite sports of some students.

Sport	Students
Football	14
Swimming	5
Athletics	9
Netball	1
Hockey	6

Show this information as a bar chart on the grid below.

[Total 3 marks]

Score:

9

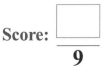

Section Seven — Statistics and Probability

Two-Way Tables

1 200 people were asked if they were right-handed or left-handed.
The table below shows some information about the results.

	Left-Handed	Right-Handed	Total
Male	9		
Female		126	140
Total	23		200

a) How many males took part in the survey?

....

[1]

b) How many left-handed females took part in the survey?

....

[1]

c) What is the ratio of left-handed people to right-handed people?

....

[2]

d) What fraction of females were left-handed?
Give your answer in its simplest form.

....

[2]

[Total 6 marks]

2 115 athletes took part in a sports day. Some took part in swimming, some took part in athletics and the rest took part in football.

63 of the athletes were boys.
10 of the athletes who swam were boys.
32 girls did athletics.
35 of the 41 athletes who played football were boys.

When you're given lots of information, putting it into a two-way table can help make it clearer.

How many girls took part in swimming?

....

[Total 4 marks]

Score:

10

Pie Charts

1 A survey was carried out at a leisure centre to find out which sport people prefer to do. The results are shown in the pie chart.

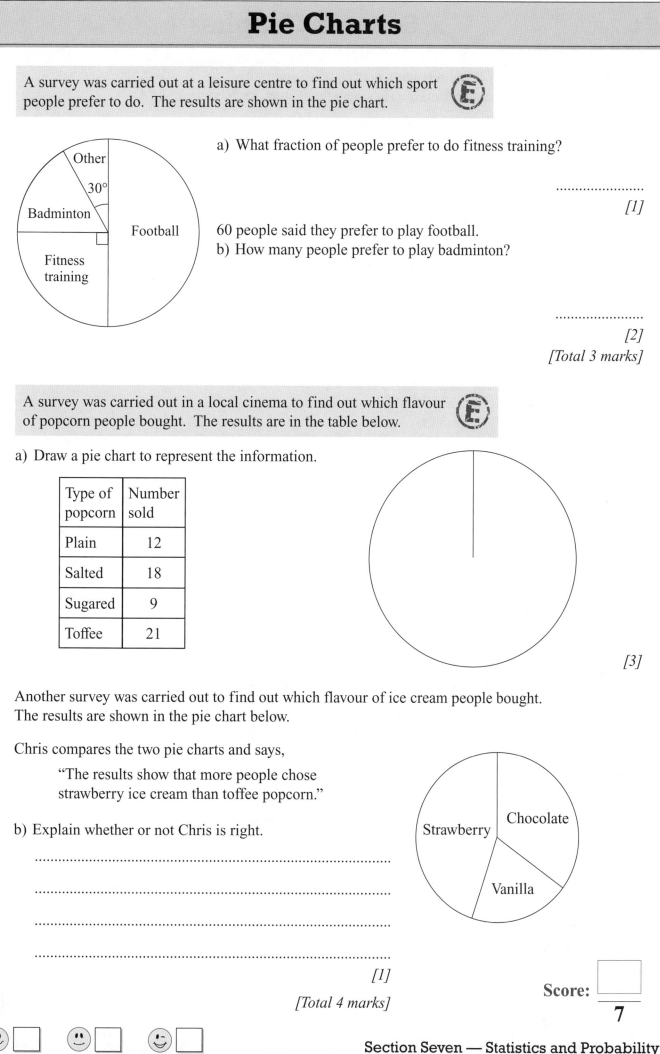

a) What fraction of people prefer to do fitness training?

....

[1]

60 people said they prefer to play football.

b) How many people prefer to play badminton?

....

[2]

[Total 3 marks]

2 A survey was carried out in a local cinema to find out which flavour of popcorn people bought. The results are in the table below.

a) Draw a pie chart to represent the information.

Type of popcorn	Number sold
Plain	12
Salted	18
Sugared	9
Toffee	21

[3]

Another survey was carried out to find out which flavour of ice cream people bought. The results are shown in the pie chart below.

Chris compares the two pie charts and says,

"The results show that more people chose strawberry ice cream than toffee popcorn."

b) Explain whether or not Chris is right.

....

....

....

....

[1]

[Total 4 marks]

Score: ☐

7

Scatter Graphs

1 In a particular class, 15 pupils study both Spanish and Italian.
Their end of year exam results are shown on the scatter graph below.

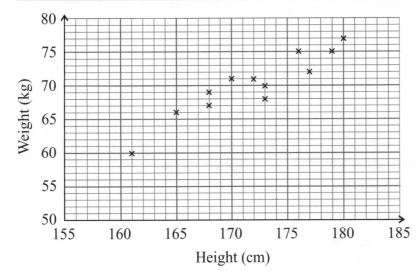

Italian (%)

Spanish (%)

a) Give the type of correlation shown
   on the graph.

   ....
   [1]

b) Draw a line of best fit for the data. *[1]*

c) Ahmed was absent for his Spanish exam
   but scored 66% on his Italian exam.
   Estimate the mark he might have
   got in Spanish.

   .... %
   [2]
   [Total 4 marks]

2 The heights and weights of boys playing in a rugby team
are shown in the scatter graph below.

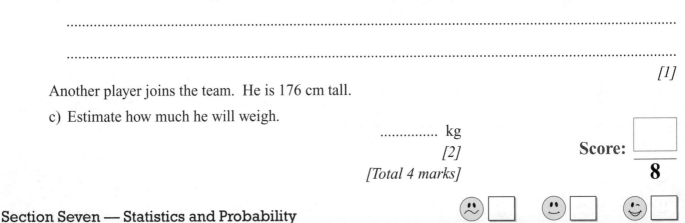

Weight (kg)

Height (cm)

Two more boys join the team.
Their heights and weights are
shown in the table below.

Player	Height (cm)	Weight (kg)
13	169	70
14	183	76

a) Show this information
   on the scatter graph. *[1]*

b) Describe the relationship between the height and weight of the players.

....

....
   [1]

Another player joins the team. He is 176 cm tall.

c) Estimate how much he will weigh.

.... kg
   [2]

   [Total 4 marks]

Score: ☐

8

Section Seven — Statistics and Probability

☹ ☐   😐 ☐   🙂 ☐

Stem and Leaf Diagrams

1 The stem and leaf diagram below shows the amount of rainfall in mm that fell on an island during a 12-day period in June. (E)

```
0 | 8
1 | 7 9
2 | 3 6 9
3 | 0 1 4 7 8
4 | 3
```

Key
0	8 means 8 mm of rain

a) Work out the median amount of rainfall.

.... mm
[1]

b) What is the range of rainfall?

.... mm
[1]

In November the median amount of rainfall was 14 mm and the range was 26 mm.

*c) Compare the amount of rainfall in November with the amount of rainfall in June.

....

....
[2]

[Total 4 marks]

2 The heights of 20 students in a class were measured to the nearest cm. (D)
The results are below.

| 165 | 163 | 159 | 148 | 162 | 167 | 155 | 158 | 173 | 169 |
| 169 | 159 | 172 | 175 | 171 | 169 | 163 | 160 | 164 | 170 |

a) Draw an ordered stem and leaf diagram to illustrate the data.

14

Key: .... | .... means .... cm

[3]

b) What is the modal height?

.... cm
[1]

c) How many of the students are less than 165 cm tall?

.... cm
[1]

[Total 5 marks]

Score:

9

Section Seven — Statistics and Probability

Frequency Tables and Averages

1 Tom is having a party and wants to know whether to serve cola, orange juice, lemonade or something else. He conducts a small survey to help him decide. He asks the question: "Which is your favourite drink — cola, orange juice, lemonade or a different drink?"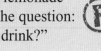

The replies are:

Orange juice	Cola	Other	Cola	Cola
Lemonade	Cola	Orange juice	Other	Orange juice
Orange juice	Cola	Lemonade	Other	Cola
Other	Cola	Other	Lemonade	Orange juice

Drink	Tally	Frequency
Cola		
Orange juice		
Lemonade		
Other		

a) Use the data to complete the table.

[2]

b) Which is the modal drink?

Remember — 'mode is most'.

....

[1]

[Total 3 marks]

2 A traffic survey at a road junction recorded the following numbers of vehicles arriving per minute.

Vehicles per minute	0	1	2	3	4
Frequency	13	8	6	2	1

a) What is the median number of vehicles per minute?

....

[2]

b) What is the mean number of vehicles per minute?

....

[3]

[Total 5 marks]

Score:

8

Grouped Frequency Tables — Averages

1 As part of their coursework, the students in a Year 11 maths class recorded their arm spans. The results are shown below.

Use the mid-interval value of each arm span group to find an estimate of the mean arm span.

Arm Span, x cm	Frequency	Mid-Interval Value	Frequency × Mid-Interval Value
$120 \leq x < 130$	13	$(120 + 130) \div 2 = 125$	$13 \times 125 =$ ....
$130 \leq x < 140$	6	$(130 + 140) \div 2 =$	$6 \times$ .... $=$ ....
$140 \leq x < 150$	4		
$150 \leq x < 160$	7		
Total			

Mean arm span = ... ÷ .... = ...

.... cm

[Total 4 marks]

2 A class of children was asked to draw a 10 cm line without a ruler, and then measure their attempt. This is a table of their results.

Length of line, x cm	Frequency
$8.5 \leq x < 9$	3
$9 \leq x < 9.5$	2
$9.5 \leq x < 10$	12
$10 \leq x < 10.5$	8
$10.5 \leq x < 11$	5

a) Which group contains the median?

....

[2]

b) What is the modal class?

....

[1]

c) Calculate an estimate of the mean length of their lines.

> Hint: you should add some extra columns to the table above to help you.

.... cm

[4]

[Total 7 marks]

Score:

11

Section Seven — Statistics and Probability

Frequency Polygons

1   The grouped frequency table below shows the number of hours of homework 30 students did in one week.

Hours of Homework, x	Frequency
$0 \leq x < 2$	15
$2 \leq x < 4$	7
$4 \leq x < 6$	5
$6 \leq x < 8$	3

Draw a frequency polygon for the data using the grid on the right.

[Total 2 marks]

2   The frequency polygons below show the amount of rainfall per day 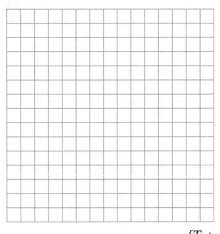 in two different towns over a period of 45 days.

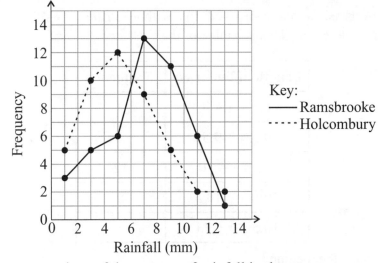

Key:
——— Ramsbrooke
----- Holcombury

a) Write down one comparison of the amount of rainfall in the two towns.

....

[1]

b) Use the frequency polygon to calculate an estimate of the mean amount of rainfall in Ramsbrooke over the 45 days.

.... mm

[3]

[Total 4 marks]

Score:

6

Probability Basics

1 Use the words below to describe the likelihood of each of the events. (F)

   Impossible   Unlikely   Even   Likely   Certain

a) Next week, the day after Wednesday will be Thursday.

....
[1]

b) When you toss a fair coin, it lands on heads.

....
[1]

c) It will snow in England next May.

....
[1]

[Total 3 marks]

2 Ellie rolls a fair 6-sided dice. (F)

a) On the scale below, mark with an arrow (↑) the probability that she will roll an odd number.

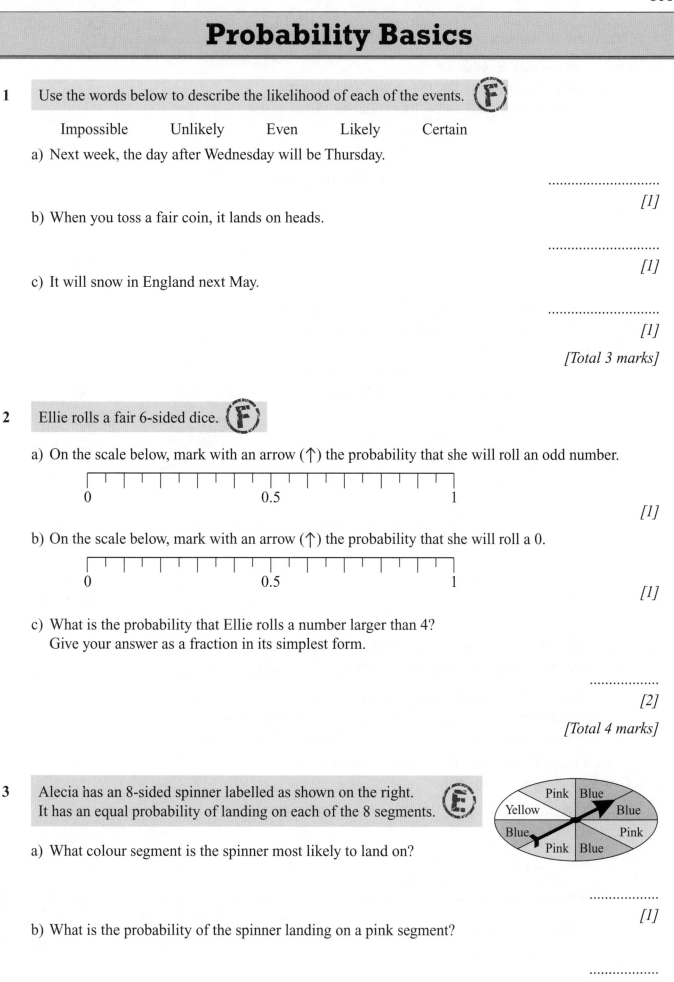

[1]

b) On the scale below, mark with an arrow (↑) the probability that she will roll a 0.

[1]

c) What is the probability that Ellie rolls a number larger than 4?
   Give your answer as a fraction in its simplest form.

....
[2]

[Total 4 marks]

3 Alecia has an 8-sided spinner labelled as shown on the right. (E)
   It has an equal probability of landing on each of the 8 segments.

a) What colour segment is the spinner most likely to land on?

....
[1]

b) What is the probability of the spinner landing on a pink segment?

....
[1]

[Total 2 marks]

4 There are 10 counters in a bag. Four of the counters are blue and the rest are red.

One counter is picked out at random.
a) Work out the probability that the counter picked is red.
   Give your answer as a fraction in its simplest form.

....

[2]

b) What is the probability that the counter picked is green?

....

[1]

[Total 3 marks]

5 Steven asks all the members of his football team whether their favourite position is in attack, midfield, defence or goal. The table below shows his results.

Position	Frequency
Attack	6
Midfield	9
Defence	4
Goal	1

A member of the team is chosen at random.

What is the probability that this person's favourite position is in midfield?

....

[Total 2 marks]

6 Sarah has stripy, spotty and plain socks in her drawer. She picks out a sock from the drawer at random.

The probability that she will pick a plain sock is 0.4.
The probability that she will pick a spotty sock from the drawer is x.
The probability that she will pick a stripy sock from the drawer is 2x.

What is the probability that the sock she picks is stripy?
Give your answer as a decimal.

P(spotty sock) = x, P(stripy sock) = 2x, P(plain sock) = O.4

.... + x + 2x = 1

.... = 1 − .... = ...

x = ... ÷ .... = ...

P(stripy sock) = 2x, so P(stripy sock) = 2 × .... = ...

....

[Total 3 marks]

Score: ☐

17

More Probability

1   Katie decides to attend two new after-school activities. She can do one on Monday **(D)** and one on Thursday. Below are lists of the activities she could do on these days.

Monday
Hockey
Orchestra
Drama

Thursday
Netball
Choir
Orienteering

List all the possible combinations of two clubs Katie could try in one week.

[Total 2 marks]

2   Alvar has a fair 6-sided dice and a set of five cards numbered 2, 4, 6, 8 and 10. **(D)**
He rolls the dice and chooses a card at random.
Alvar adds the number on the dice to the number on the card to calculate his total score.

a) Complete the table below to show all of the possible scores.

Cards

Dice		2	4	6	8	10
	1					
	2					12
	3				11	13
	4			10	12	14
	5		9	11	13	15
	6	8	10	12	14	16

[2]

b) Find the probability that Alvar will score exactly 9.
Give your answer as a fraction in its simplest form.

....

[2]

[Total 4 marks]

Score

6

Expected Frequency

1 The probability of a train arriving in Udderston on time is 0.64.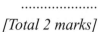

Hester gets the train to Udderston 200 times a year.
How many times a year can Hester expect to arrive at the station on time?

.... × 0.64 = ...

....
[Total 2 marks]

2 A bowling alley has green, purple, orange, blue and pink balls. **D**

The probabilities that a ball chosen at random will be green, purple, orange, blue or pink are shown below.

Colour	Green	Purple	Orange	Blue	Pink
Probability	0.35	0.1	0.3	0.05	0.2

The bowling alley has 400 balls. Estimate the number of green balls.

....
[Total 2 marks]

3 Here is a 5-sided spinner. **D**
The spinner is biased.

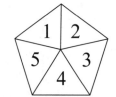

The probability that the spinner will land on the numbers 1 to 4 is given in this table.
I spin the spinner 100 times.

Number	1	2	3	4	5
Probability	0.3	0.15	0.2	0.25	

Estimate the number of times it will land on 5.

....
[Total 4 marks]

Score: ☐

8

Relative Frequency

1 Suda has a 6-sided dice. The sides are numbered 1 to 6. (C)

Suda rolls the dice 50 times and records the results in the table below.

Number	1	2	3	4	5	6
Relative Frequency	0.32	0.12	0.24	0.14	0.06	0.12

a) How many times did she roll a 6?

....

[2]

b) Is Suda's dice fair? Explain your answer.

....

....

[2]

c) She rolls the dice another 50 times. Should she expect the same results? Explain your answer.

....

....

[1]

[Total 5 marks]

2 Cameron has a bag containing a large number of counters. (C)
They are each numbered with a number from 1 to 5.

He selects one counter at random from the bag, records its number, and then puts it back in the bag.
Cameron does this 100 times. He records his results in the table below.

Number on counter	1	2	3	4	5
Frequency	23	25	22	21	9
Relative frequency					

a) Complete the table, giving the relative frequencies of selecting each number.

[2]

Cameron thinks there is the same number of counters with each number on in the bag.

b) Is he right? Give a reason for your answer

....

....

[1]

[Total 3 marks]

Exam Practice Tip

Try not to confuse expected and relative frequency. Expected frequency is the number of times you expect
something to happen when you know its probability. Relative frequency is an estimate of the probability using
results from an experiment.

Score

8

Section Seven — Statistics and Probability

Candidate Surname		Candidate Forename(s)	

Centre Number	Candidate Number	Candidate Signature

GCSE

Mathematics A
Paper 1 (Non-Calculator)

Foundation Tier

Practice Paper
Time allowed: 1 hour 45 minutes

You must have:
Pen, pencil, eraser, ruler, protractor, pair of compasses.
You may use tracing paper.

You are **not allowed** to use a calculator.

Instructions to candidates
- Use **black** ink to write your answers.
- Write your name and other details in the spaces provided above.
- Answer **all** questions in the spaces provided.
- In calculations show clearly how you worked out your answers.
- Do all rough work on the paper.

Information for candidates
- The marks available are given in brackets at the end of each question.
- You may get marks for method, even if your answer is incorrect.
- There are 27 questions in this paper. There are no blank pages.
- There are 100 marks available for this paper.
- In questions labelled with an asterisk (*), you will be assessed
  on the quality of your written communication — take particular
  care here with spelling, punctuation and the quality of explanations.

Get the answers — on video and in print

Your free Online Edition of this book includes a link to step-by-step video solutions
for this Exam Paper, plus worked solutions you can print out.
There's more info about how to get your Online Edition at the front of this book.

Answer ALL the questions.

Write your answers in the spaces provided.

You must show all of your working.

1   (a)   What is the value of the 7 in the number 13 973?

....
[1]

(b)   Round the number 331 to the nearest 10

....
[1]

(c)   Write out the number 1758 in words.

....
[1]

(d)   Write 85.7 to the nearest whole number.

....
[1]

[Total 4 marks]

2   (a)   Reflect the shaded shape in the mirror line.

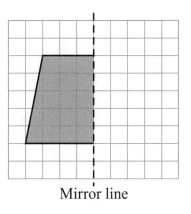

Mirror line

[1]

(b)   Here is a shape with rotational symmetry.

Write down the order of rotational symmetry of this shape.

....
[1]

[Total 2 marks]

Practice Paper 1

3 (a) Work out 7.55×10

....

[1]

(b) Work out $427.3 \div 100$

....

[1]

(c) Work out 0.302×1000

....

[1]

[Total 3 marks]

---

4 Sam needs to buy grammar books and dictionaries for a class of students.
She needs 15 copies of each. She sees them on sale at a local book shop.

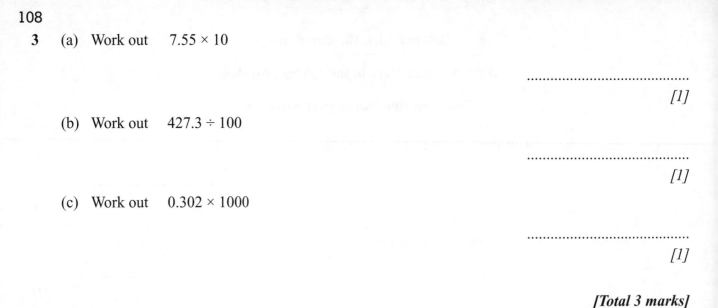

(a) Calculate how much it would cost Sam to buy all the books for her class from the shop.

£ ....

[2]

(b) A website sells a set of the same grammar book and dictionary together for £4.
The website has a £5 delivery charge.
Should Sam buy the books from the shop or the website? Explain your answer.

....

....

....

[2]

[Total 4 marks]

2

5   A group of people were asked what they had eaten for breakfast that morning.
    The incomplete bar chart below shows some of the results.

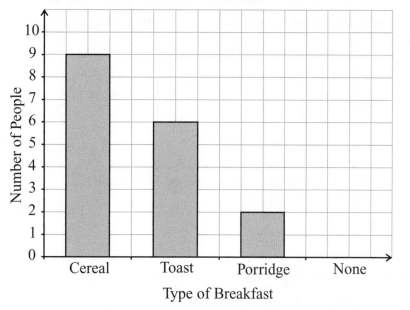

(a) How many people had porridge for breakfast?

    ....
    [1]

(b) Write down how many more people had cereal for breakfast than toast.

    ....
    [2]

(c) Five people said that they didn't have any breakfast.
     Use this information to complete the bar chart.

    [1]

(d) Which type of breakfast was the mode?

    ....
    [1]

[Total 5 marks]

6   A clothes shop has 112 shirts in stock.
    On Monday it sells 17 shirts, and on Tuesday morning it gets a delivery of 38 shirts.
    How many shirts does it have after the delivery arrives on Tuesday?

    ....
    [Total 2 marks]

Practice Paper 1

7   Use the words below to describe the likelihood of each of the events.

Impossible   Unlikely   Even   Likely   Certain

(a)   A card drawn at random from a pack of playing cards is a two of diamonds.

....

[1]

(b)   Christmas will fall in November next year.

....

[1]

(c)   When you roll a fair six-sided dice, it lands on an even number.

....

[1]

[Total 3 marks]

8   The shape is drawn on a grid of centimetre squares.

(a)   What is the perimeter of the shape?

.... cm

[1]

(b)   What is the area of the shape? Make sure you give the units of your answer.

....

[2]

[Total 3 marks]

9   The picture shows a man standing next to an elephant.

Estimate the height of the elephant.

.... m

[Total 3 marks]

4

10 The table shows the temperatures in Glasgow and Barcelona at different times on the same day.

Time	Temperature in Glasgow (°C)	Temperature in Barcelona (°C)
04 00	−8	6
08 00	−2	9
12 00	3	15
16 00	1	14
20 00	−3	11

(a) Write down the maximum temperature across the two cities.

.... °C

[1]

(b) How much colder was Glasgow than Barcelona at 08 00?

.... °C

[2]

(c) What was the difference between the highest temperature in Glasgow
and the lowest temperature in Barcelona?

.... °C

[3]

[Total 6 marks]

---

11 Look at the triangles below.

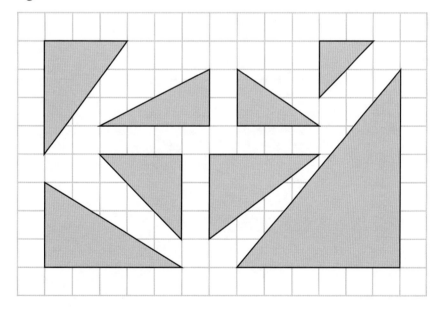

(a) Write C in the two triangles that are **congruent**.

[1]

(b) Write S in the two triangles that are **similar**.

[1]

[Total 2 marks]

5

12 Arthur thinks of three different numbers. The numbers have a range of 6 and a mean of 5.
What are the three numbers?

.............., ..., ...

[Total 2 marks]

13 For each of the statements below, choose a number from the list which matches the description.

19   125   36   18   84   32   124   48

(a) An even number less than 29.

....

[1]

(b) A power of 2.

....

[1]

(c) A square number.

....

[1]

(d) A cube number.

....

[1]

[Total 4 marks]

6

14 Below is part of a bus timetable.

Windsor	08 12	08 46	09 08	09 33
Datchet	08 17	08 51	09 13	09 38
Old Windsor	08 23	08 57	09 19	09 44
Egham	08 33	09 07	09 29	09 54
Staines-upon-Thames	08 40	09 14	09 36	10 01
Chertsey	08 52	09 26	09 48	10 13
Weybridge	09 01	09 35	09 57	10 22

(a) (i) A bus leaves Datchet at 08 51.
What time should it arrive in Weybridge?

....

(ii) A later bus leaves Old Windsor at 09 44.
How long should it take to travel to Chertsey?

.... minutes

[3]

(b) Jake has a bus pass that gives him $\frac{1}{3}$ off the price of bus tickets.

He buys a return ticket from Windsor to Egham.
The normal price of the ticket is £3.60.

How much does Jake pay?

£ ....

[2]

[Total 5 marks]

15 Work out the value of:
(a) $8 \times 2 + 7$

....

[1]

(b) 2^3

....

[1]

(c) $\sqrt{49}$

....

[1]

[Total 3 marks]

*16 For work one week, Hassan drives 75 miles each day for 4 days.
He is able to claim in expenses 20p for every mile he drives.

Calculate the amount, in pounds, that he can claim in expenses for his working week.

£ ....

[Total 3 marks]

---

17 A quadrilateral has been drawn on the grid.

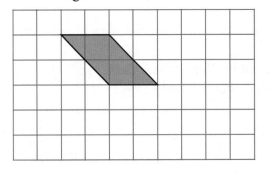

(a) Write down the name of this quadrilateral.

....

[1]

(b) Show how this quadrilateral can tessellate on the grid.
You should draw at least 6 quadrilaterals.

[2]

[Total 3 marks]

18 (a) Complete the table of values for $y = 2 + 2x$.

x	−1	0	1	2	3	4
y	0				8	10

[2]

(b) On the grid below, draw the graph of $y = 2 + 2x$.

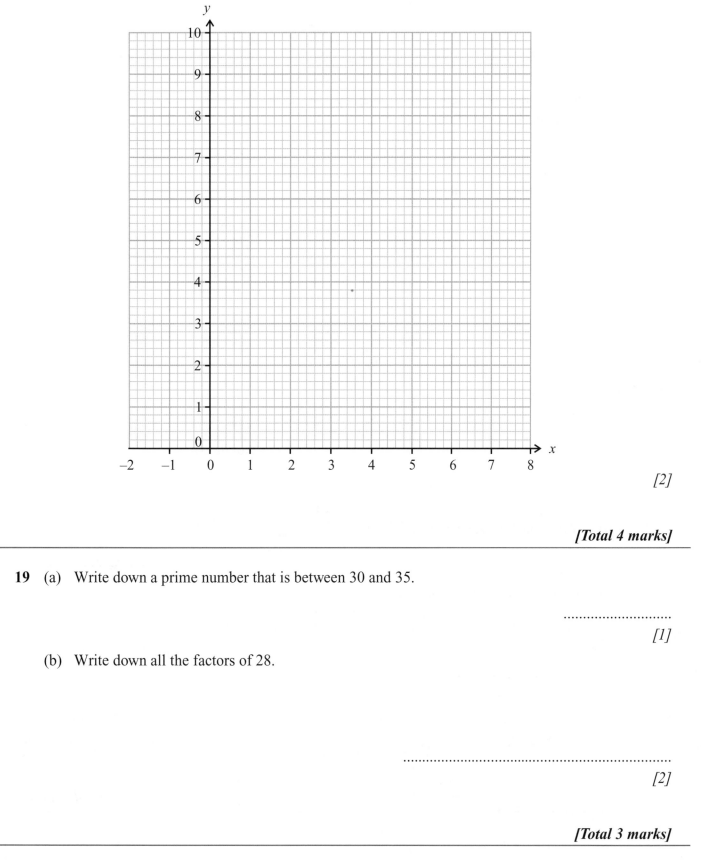

[2]

[Total 4 marks]

19 (a) Write down a prime number that is between 30 and 35.

....
[1]

(b) Write down all the factors of 28.

....
[2]

[Total 3 marks]

20 (a) Here are the first five terms of a number sequence.

57   46   35   24   13

(i) Write down the next number in the sequence.

....

(ii) Explain how you found your answer.

....

....

[2]

(b) The nth term of another sequence is given by $2n + 2$.
(i) Find the 4th term of this sequence.

....

*(ii) Rita says that the number 65 will be in the sequence.
Is she correct? Explain your answer.

....

....

[3]

[Total 5 marks]

21 Here is a right-angled triangle.

50°

6 cm

Not drawn
to scale

a

8 cm

*(a) (i) Work out the size of angle a.

.... °

(ii) Give a reason for your answer.

....

[2]

(b) Work out the area of the triangle.

.... cm²

[2]

[Total 4 marks]

22 a)   Solve $3x = 21$

$x =$ ....
[1]

b)   Solve $2m + 5 = -9$

$m =$ ....
[2]

c)   Solve $5n - 11 = 2n + 4$

$n =$ ....
[2]

[Total 5 marks]

23   Robert is the conductor of a choir that is performing a concert for charity.

Robert needs to buy sheet music for each of the 40 singers in the choir.
A website offers the sheet music for £7.00 per copy
with a 10% discount for an order of 10 or more copies.
Robert also has to pay £318 to rent the venue for the concert.

Robert sells 95 tickets for the concert. A ticket for the concert costs £10.

Robert has agreed to donate 50% of the concert profits to charity.
How much money should he donate to charity?

£ ....

[Total 7 marks]

11

24 (a) Expand and simplify $3(2 + b) + 5(3 - b)$

....

[2]

(b) Factorise $6c - 8$

....

[1]

(c) Factorise fully $2d^2 + 10d$

....

[2]

[Total 5 marks]

*25 A Youth Centre decides to organise a trip to a theme park.
They plan to hire a coach that costs £100 for the day.
The cost to get into the theme park is £15 per person.

The Youth Centre will charge £23 per person for the trip,
which includes the coach journey and entry to the theme park.

The trip can only go ahead if the Youth Centre makes enough money to cover its costs.
Work out how many people need to go on the trip for it to go ahead.

....

[Total 4 marks]

26 A large supermarket chain is planning to open a new store in Digton.
Residents of Digton are asked to complete a questionnaire to give their views on the idea.

This is one of the questions from the questionnaire.

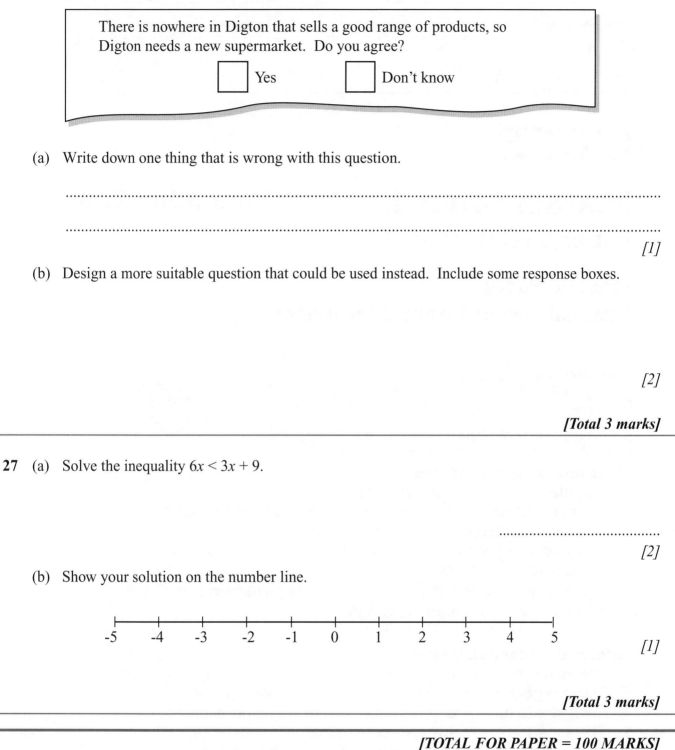

There is nowhere in Digton that sells a good range of products, so
Digton needs a new supermarket. Do you agree?

☐ Yes   ☐ Don't know

(a) Write down one thing that is wrong with this question.

....

....

[1]

(b) Design a more suitable question that could be used instead. Include some response boxes.

[2]

[Total 3 marks]

27 (a) Solve the inequality $6x < 3x + 9$.

....

[2]

(b) Show your solution on the number line.

$$\begin{array}{ccccccccccc} | & | & | & | & | & | & | & | & | & | & | \\ -5 & -4 & -3 & -2 & -1 & 0 & 1 & 2 & 3 & 4 & 5 \end{array}$$

[1]

[Total 3 marks]

[TOTAL FOR PAPER = 100 MARKS]

Practice Paper 1

Candidate Surname		Candidate Forename(s)	

Centre Number	Candidate Number	Candidate Signature

GCSE

Mathematics A
Paper 2 (Calculator)

Foundation Tier

Practice Paper
Time allowed: 1 hour 45 minutes

You must have:
Pen, pencil, eraser, ruler, protractor, pair of compasses.
You may use tracing paper.

You **may use** a calculator.

Instructions to candidates
- Use **black** ink to write your answers.
- Write your name and other details in the spaces provided above.
- Answer **all** questions in the spaces provided.
- In calculations show clearly how you worked out your answers.
- Do all rough work on the paper.
- Unless a question tells you otherwise, take the value of π to be 3.142, or use the π button on your calculator.

Information for candidates
- The marks available are given in brackets at the end of each question.
- You may get marks for method, even if your answer is incorrect.
- There are 25 questions in this paper. There are no blank pages.
- There are 100 marks available for this paper.
- In questions labelled with an asterisk (*), you will be assessed on the quality of your written communication — take particular care here with spelling, punctuation and the quality of explanations.

Get the answers — on video and in print
Your free Online Edition of this book includes a link to step-by-step video solutions for this Exam Paper, plus worked solutions you can print out.
There's more info about how to get your Online Edition at the front of this book.

Answer ALL the questions.

Write your answers in the spaces provided.

You must show all of your working.

1 (a) Write twenty four thousand and twelve in digits.

....

[1]

(b) Put the following numbers in order of size, from smallest to largest.

85.3   95.3   85.03   90.9   87.2

.... , ... , ... , ... , ...

[1]

Jill has 4 cards, each with a number written on.

| 5 | | 9 | | 6 | | 2 |

She lines all of the cards up to make a 4 digit number.

(c) (i) What is the largest number she can make?

....

(ii) What is the smallest number she can make?

....

[2]

[Total 4 marks]

2 The diagram below shows a quadrilateral.

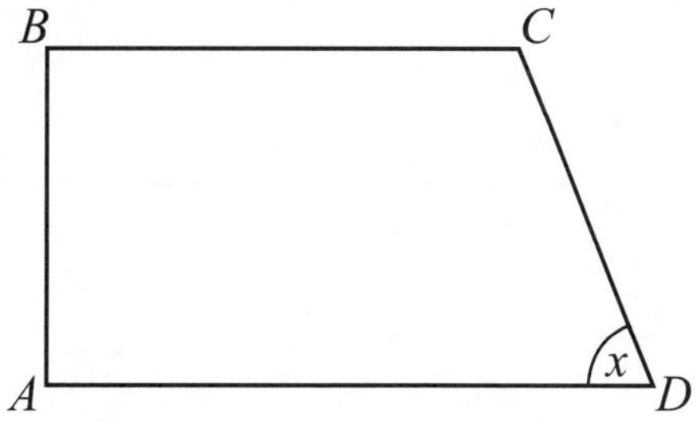

(a) Measure the length of *AB*.

.... cm

[1]

(b) On the diagram, mark the midpoint of the line *AB* with a cross.

[1]

(c) Mark a right angle with the letter R.

[1]

(d) Give the mathematical name for the type of angle marked *x*.

....

[1]

[Total 4 marks]

1

3 (a) Write down the fraction of this shape that is shaded.

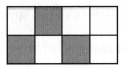

....

[1]

(b) Write down the fraction of the shape that is shaded.
Give your answer in its simplest form.

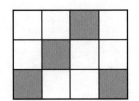

....

[2]

(c) (i) Shade 10% of this shape.

(ii) Write down the proportion of the shape that is **not** shaded.
Give your answer as a decimal.

....

[2]

[Total 5 marks]

4   The pictogram shows the number of pies eaten by customers at a restaurant one week.

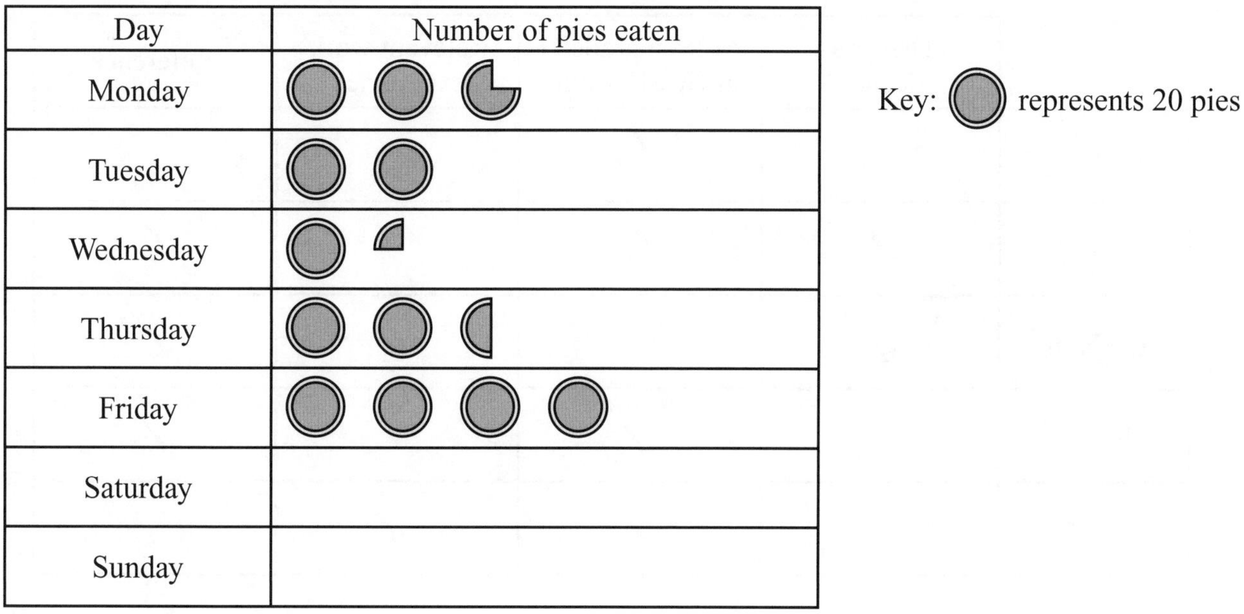

Day	Number of pies eaten
Monday	◉ ◉ ◕
Tuesday	◉ ◉
Wednesday	◉ ◣
Thursday	◉ ◉ ◖
Friday	◉ ◉ ◉ ◉
Saturday	
Sunday	

Key: ◉ represents 20 pies

(a)   How many pies were eaten on Monday?

....

[1]

(b)   How many more pies were eaten on Thursday than on Wednesday?

....

[1]

90 pies were eaten on Saturday.
35 pies were eaten on Sunday.

(c)   Complete the pictogram using this information.

[2]

[Total 4 marks]

3

Practice Paper 2

5   The table below gives some information about five candidates who have applied for a job as a postal worker.

	Driver's licence	At least grade G in GCSE Maths	Relevant work experience	Reference
Edward		✓		
Fiona	✓	✓		✓
Graham	✓		✓	✓
Nadia		✓		✓
Isaac		✓	✓	

(a)   Which candidates have at least a grade G in GCSE Maths?

....

[1]

(b)   Write down all the information from the table about Graham.

....

....

[1]

(c)   Write down the fraction of candidates who have relevant work experience.

....

[1]

[Total 3 marks]

6 Daisy is monitoring the amount of rainfall (in cm) each month in the towns of Duluth and Norcross. Her results for a six-month period are shown in the table below.

Month	April	May	June	July	August	September
Duluth (cm of rain)	6	3	5	6	7	10
Norcross (cm of rain)	5	4	4	8	7	8

Draw a suitable chart or diagram that could be used to compare the numbers of centimetres of rain each month in the two towns.

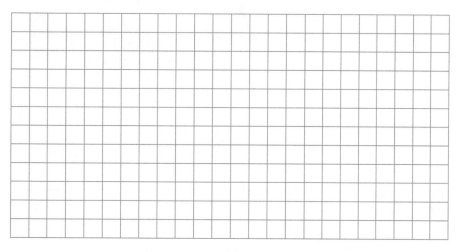

[Total 4 marks]

7 (a) Write down the mathematical name of each shape

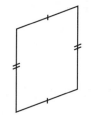
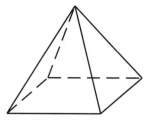

(i) .... (ii) .... *[2]*

(b) Here is a 3D shape.

(i) Write down the number of faces of the shape.

....

(ii) Write down the number of edges of the shape.

....

[2]

[Total 4 marks]

5

Practice Paper 2

8 Complete the pattern so that it has rotational symmetry of order 4.

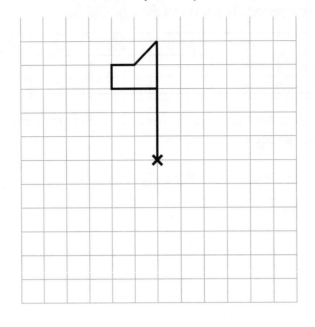

[Total 2 marks]

9 Look at the coordinate grid.

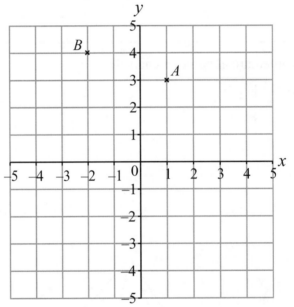

(a) Write down the coordinates of point *A*.

(...................., ...)
[1]

(b) Write down the coordinates of point *B*.

(...................., ...)
[1]

(c) Plot the point (−3, −4) on the grid. Label this point *C*.

[1]

[Total 3 marks]

10 Jemma is the manager of a shoe shop.
One week Jemma recorded the size of each pair of a particular type of shoe that was sold.

Here are her results.

6   4   7   6   4   8   4

(a) Write down the modal size sold.

....

[1]

(b) Work out the median size sold.

....

[2]

(c) Explain why Jemma might be more interested in the modal size sold than the median size.

....

....

[1]

[Total 4 marks]

11   Andrew runs a snack shop. These are the prices for some of the snacks he sells.

Price list	
Chocolate bar	£0.70
Crisps	£0.35
Flapjack	£0.95
Cereal bar	£1.10
Apple	£0.50

(a) How much does it cost to buy a chocolate bar, a cereal bar and a flapjack?

£ ....

[1]

(b) A customer buys two packets of crisps and an apple. They pay with a £5 note.
How much change should Andrew give them?

£ ....

[2]

(c) Next week, Andrew is going to put all of his prices up by 20%.
How much will it cost to buy a cereal bar and an apple next week?

£ ....

[3]

[Total 6 marks]

7

Practice Paper 2

12 (a) Write down the number shown by the arrow.

....

[1]

(b) Find the number 84 on the number line.
Mark it with an arrow.

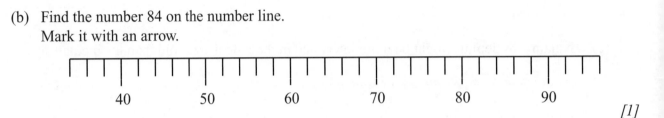

[1]

[Total 2 marks]

13 Mark is following a recipe for roasting a chicken.
The recipe gives the following information on the cooking time for a chicken:

"Cook the chicken for 50 minutes per kg, plus an extra 20 minutes."

(a) Mark has bought a chicken that weighs 2.4 kg.
Calculate how long he should cook the chicken for.

.... hours .... minutes

[2]

Mark is also making a salad to go with his chicken.

Salad Dressing: Serves 4
3 tablespoons olive oil
1 tablespoon vinegar
Seasoning

(b) Mark wants to make a salad dressing for six people using the recipe above.
How much olive oil should he use?

.... tablespoons

[1]

[Total 3 marks]

14

Diagram not accurately drawn

(a) Write down the size of angle *a* and give a reason for your answer.

....

[2]

(b) Work out the size of angle *b*.

.... °

[2]

[Total 4 marks]

15 In a probability experiment, Amanda flips an ordinary coin and notes the result.
Then she rolls an ordinary unbiased 6-sided dice and notes the result.

(a) List all the possible combinations she could get.

....

....

[2]

Amanda flips the coin and rolls the dice.

(b) Work out the probability that Amanda gets heads on the coin **and** a 3 on the dice.

....

[1]

(c) Work out the probability that she gets heads on the coin **and** a 3 or higher on the dice.
Give your answer as a fraction in its simplest form.

....

[2]

[Total 5 marks]

Practice Paper 2

130

16 $e = 3, f = 5$ and $g = -7$

Find the value of

(a) $e^2 + g^2$

....
[2]

(b) $\dfrac{efg}{2}$

....
[2]

[Total 4 marks]

17 Below is a scale drawing of Sharon's kitchen.

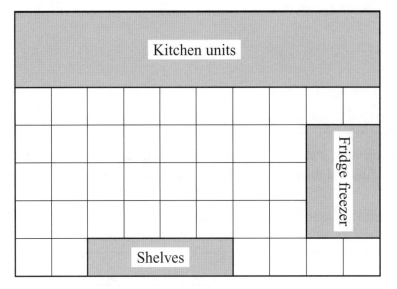

(a) The shelves are 2 m long and 0.5 m wide. What is the scale of the drawing?

1 cm to .... m
[1]

(b) What is the area of the real kitchen?

.... m²
[3]

[Total 4 marks]

10

18 The graph below can be used to convert between pounds (£) and euros (€).

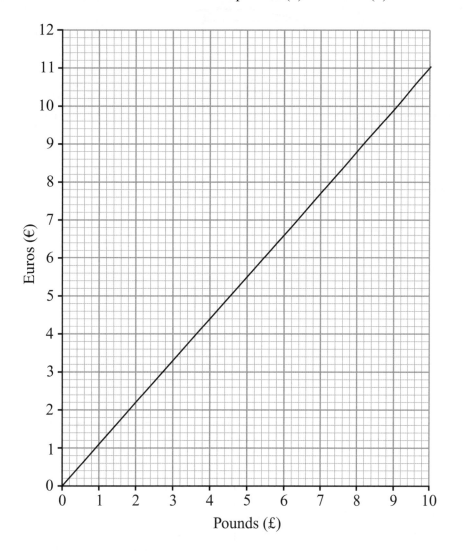

(a) Use the graph to convert £2 to euros.

€ ....
[1]

(b) Use the graph to convert €3 to pounds.

£ ....
[1]

(c) Use the graph to work out how much £20 is in euros.

€ ....
[2]

[Total 4 marks]

11

19 The diagram shows a cuboid.

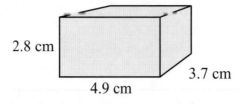

Diagram not
accurately drawn

2.8 cm

3.7 cm

4.9 cm

(a) Calculate the volume of the cuboid. Include the correct units in your answer.

....

[3]

Another cuboid has a volume of 56 cm³, a width of 4 cm and a length of 7 cm.

(b) Calculate h, the height of the cuboid.

.... cm

[2]

[Total 5 marks]

20 (a) Reflect shape **A** in the line $x = 1$. Label your shape **B**.

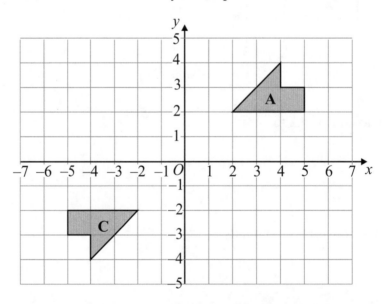

[2]

(b) Describe fully the single transformation that maps shape **C** onto shape **A**.

....

....

....

[3]

[Total 5 marks]

21 A painter wants to calculate the cost of painting the four outside walls of a warehouse.
The diagram below gives the dimensions of the warehouse.

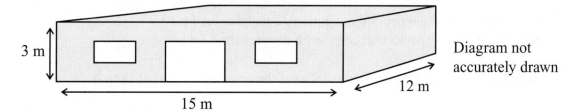

3 m

15 m

12 m

Diagram not
accurately drawn

There are 5 windows in the warehouse that each measure 2 m by 1 m and
a door that measures 3 m by 2.5 m.

The paint covers 13 m² per litre.
The paint can be bought in tins that contain 5 litres or 2.5 litres.
5 litre tins cost £20.99
2.5 litre tins cost £12.99

Calculate the cheapest price for painting the warehouse. You must show all your working.

£ ....

[Total 6 marks]

22 The equation $x^3 - x - 4 = 0$ has a solution between 1 and 2.

Use trial and improvement to find this solution.
Give your answer correct to one decimal place.

You must show **ALL** of your working.

$x =$ ....

[Total 4 marks]

*23 Tom is buying nappies for his son.
He can buy nappies from two different shops

Shop A sells medium packs that contain 32 nappies for £6.40,
Shop B sells large packs that contain 56 nappies for £7.84.

Tom has a voucher that gives him 25% off the price of nappies at shop A.

Should Tom buy the nappies at shop A or shop B?
You must show all your working.

[Total 4 marks]

---

24 Simplify:

(a) $a^4 \times a^5$

....
[1]

(b) $b^9 \div b^3$

....
[1]

[Total 2 marks]

---

25 (a) The diagram shows a right-angled triangle.

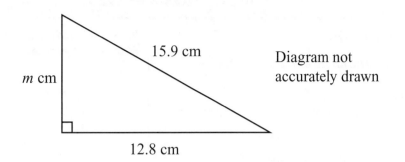

15.9 cm

Diagram not
accurately drawn

m cm

12.8 cm

Calculate the value of *m*. Give your answer correct to 1 decimal place.

....

[2]

*(b) Explain why triangle *ABC* below cannot be a right-angled triangle.

C

8.1 m

14.5 m

Diagram not
accurately drawn

B

15.6 m

A

....

....

....

....

....

[3]

[Total 5 marks]

[TOTAL FOR PAPER = 100 MARKS]

Practice Paper 2

Answers

Section One — Numbers

Pages 4-5: Ordering Numbers and Place Value

1 a) 58 *[1 mark]*
   b) 530 *[1 mark]*
   c)

   [1 mark]

2 a) Five thousand and seventy-nine *[1 mark]*
   b) 6105 *[1 mark]*
   c) 90/ninety *[1 mark]*

3 a) Twenty-six thousand and four *[1 mark]*
   b) 20 364 *[1 mark]*
   c) 800/eight hundred *[1 mark]*

4 a) Four hundred and twenty thousand, four hundred
        and fifty-seven *[1 mark]*
   b) 6 000 000 *[1 mark]*
   c) 2000/two thousand *[1 mark]*

5 98 649, 98 653, 100 003, 100 010 *[1 mark]*

6 53.3, 52.91, 35.6, 35.54, 35.06 *[1 mark]*

7 a) 12 478 *[1 mark]*
   b) 87 421 *[1 mark]*

Pages 6-7: Addition and Subtraction

1 $522 - (197 + 24) = 301$
   *[2 marks available — 1 mark for subtracting the two numbers
   from 522, 1 mark for the correct answer]*

2 £290 + £59 + £39 + £95 = £483
   *[3 marks available — 1 mark for finding the correct costs,
   1 mark for adding them together, 1 mark for the correct answer]*

3 £15 − £8.50 + £20 − £18 = £8.50, so he would not have
   £10 to give to his sister.
   *[2 marks available — 1 mark for adding and subtracting the
   correct amounts to work out how much he would have left,
   1 mark for the correct conclusion]*

4 Total cost = £2.15 + £2.40 + £2.40 = £6.95
   Change = £10 − £6.95 = £3.05
   *[2 marks available — 1 mark for adding amounts and
   subtracting from £10, 1 mark for the correct answer]*

5 a) E.g. Toast (2 slices) and coffee, or yoghurt with fruit and tea.
        *[2 marks available — 2 marks for 2 correct combinations
        and no incorrect combinations, otherwise 1 mark for
        1 correct combination]*
        *Parvati could also buy toast (2 slices) and tea or
        toast (2 slices) and fresh orange juice.*
   b) £3.40 + £2.30 + £1.40 + £1.50 = £8.60
        £10 − £8.60 = £1.40
        *[3 marks available — 1 mark for finding the correct costs,
        1 mark for adding them together and subtracting from £10,
        1 mark for the correct answer]*

Page 8: Multiplying and Dividing by 10, 100, etc.

1 a) 32.8 × 10 = 328 *[1 mark]*
   b) 429 ÷ 10 = 42.9 *[1 mark]*
   c) 22.2 × 1000 = 22 200 *[1 mark]*

2 a) 4.268 × 100 = 426.8 *[1 mark]*
   b) 304 ÷ 100 = 3.04 *[1 mark]*
   c) 2470 ÷ 1000 = 2.47 *[1 mark]*

3 a) 23 × 100 000 = 2 300 000 *[1 mark]*
   b) 46 000 ÷ 100 = 460 *[1 mark]*

Pages 9-10: Multiplying and Dividing Without a Calculator

1 a)
$$\begin{array}{r} 113 \\ \times\ 76 \\ \hline 678 \\ +\ 7910 \\ \hline 8588 \end{array}$$
   *[2 marks available — 1 mark for a correct method,
   1 mark for the correct answer]*
   *"A correct method" here can be any non-calculator
   multiplication method.*

   b)
$$\begin{array}{r} 376 \\ \times\ 48 \\ \hline 3008 \\ +\ 15040 \\ \hline 18048 \end{array}$$
   *[2 marks available — 1 mark for a correct method,
   1 mark for the correct answer]*

2 a) $19 + 26 \div 2 = 19 + 13 = 32$
        *[2 marks available — 1 mark for doing the calculation
        steps in the correct order, 1 mark for the correct answer]*
   b) $(22 - 18) \times (3 + 8) = 4 \times 11 = 44$
        *[2 marks available — 1 mark for doing the calculation
        steps in the correct order, 1 mark for the correct answer]*

3 Total miles travelled = $(30 \times 2) + (28 \times 2) + (39 \times 2) + (40 \times 2)$
                        $= 60 + 56 + 78 + 80$
                        $= 274$ miles
   Expenses for miles travelled = 274 × 30p = 8220p = £82.20
   Expenses for food = 4 × £8 = £32
   Total expenses = £82.20 + £32 = £114.20
   *[5 marks available — 1 mark for multiplying the distances by 2,
   1 mark for finding total miles, 1 mark for multiplying total
   miles by 30 or 0.3(0), 1 mark for finding food expenses,
   1 mark for the correct final answer]*

4 $$54 \overline{)75^{21}6}\ \ \ \begin{array}{c}1\ 4\end{array}$$
   So 756 ÷ 54 = 14
   *[2 marks available — 1 mark for any division method,
   1 mark for the correct answer]*

5 £200 − £5 = £195
   $$15 \overline{)19^4 5}\ \ \ \begin{array}{c}13\end{array}$$, so each ticket costs £13
   *[3 marks available — 1 mark for subtracting £5 from £200,
   1 mark for dividing £195 by 15, 1 mark for the correct
   final answer]*

6 Slices of pizza he needs = 15 × 3 = 45 *[1 mark]*
   Number of pizzas he needs = 45 ÷ 8 *[1 mark]*
                            = 5.625
   So he needs 6 pizzas *[1 mark]*
   A 300 g packet of crisps is enough for 300 ÷ 25 = 12 people *[1 mark]*
   So James needs 2 packets of crisps *[1 mark]*
   [5 marks available in total — as above]

Page 11: Multiplying and Dividing with Decimals

1 a)
$$\begin{array}{r} 16 \\ \times\ 7 \\ \hline 112 \end{array}$$
   16 × 0.7 has one digit after the decimal point,
   so 16 × 0.7 = 11.2
   *[2 marks available — 1 mark for a correct method,
   1 mark for the correct answer]*
   "A correct method" can be any non-calculator multiplication method.

b)
$$\begin{array}{r} 25 \\ \times\ 19 \\ \hline 225 \\ +\ 250 \\ \hline 475 \end{array}$$
25 × 1.9 has one digit after the decimal point,
so 25 × 1.9 = 47.5
[2 marks available — 1 mark for a correct method,
1 mark for the correct answer]

2 a) $5.6 × 4.27 = (23\ 912 ÷ 10) ÷ 100 = 23.912$ *[1 mark]*

b) $0.56 × 4\ 270\ 000 = (23\ 912 ÷ 100) × 10\ 000 = 2\ 391\ 200$
[1 mark]

c) $2391.2 ÷ 4.27 = (56 ÷ 10) × 100 = 560$ *[1 mark]*

3 $7 × 8 = 56$
$0.7 × 0.8$ has two digits after the decimal point,
so $0.7 × 0.8 = 0.56$
[2 marks available — 1 mark for a correct method,
1 mark for the correct answer]

4 a) $14 ÷ 0.7 = \dfrac{14}{0.7} = \dfrac{140}{7} = 20$
[2 marks available — 1 mark for a correct method,
1 mark for the correct answer]

b) $23 ÷ 0.46 = \dfrac{23}{0.46} = \dfrac{2300}{46} = 50$
[2 marks available — 1 mark for a correct method,
1 mark for the correct answer]

Page 12: Negative Numbers

1 −103.1, −102.7, −102.4, −99.8 , −98.9, 98.9, 99.5 *[1 mark]*

2 a) $9 − 4 = 5\ °C$ *[1 mark]*

b) St Petersburg *[1 mark]*

c) $22 − (−8) = 30\ °C$
[3 marks available — 1 mark for finding the correct values,
1 mark for subtracting, 1 mark for the correct answer]

3 a) $−11 × 7 = −77$ *[1 mark]*

b) $−72 ÷ −8 = 9$ *[1 mark]*

Page 13: Special Types of Number

1 a) 41 *[1 mark]*

b) 100 *[1 mark]*

c) 27 *[1 mark]*

2 a) 81 *[1 mark]*

b) 64 *[1 mark]*

c) 6 *[1 mark]*

Page 14: Prime Numbers, Multiples and Factors

1 a) 7 or 11 *[1 mark for either]*

b) 15 *[1 mark]*

c) 15 *[1 mark]*

d) 1 and 12, or 7 and 12, or 11 and 12
[1 mark available — 1 mark maximum for any of the three
options above]

2 a) 1, 2, 4, 5, 10, 20
[2 marks available — 2 marks if all 6 factors are correct
and no extra incorrect factors have been included,
otherwise 1 mark if all 6 factors are correct but 1 extra
incorrect factor has been included, or if at least 4 factors are
correct and there are no more than 6 numbers listed in total]

b) 56, 64 *[1 mark]*

3 a) E.g. 21, 42 *[1 mark for any two multiples of 21]*

b) 47 *[1 mark]*

Page 15: Prime Factors, LCM and HCF

1 a)
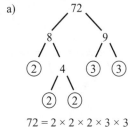
$72 = 2 × 2 × 2 × 3 × 3$
[2 marks available — 1 mark for a correct method,
1 mark for all prime factors correct]

b) Factors of 54 are: 1, 2, 3, 6, 9, ⑱, 27, 54
Factors of 72 are: 1, 2, 3, 4, 6, 8, 9, 12, ⑱, 24, 36, 72
So the highest common factor (HCF) is 18 *[1 mark]*

You could use the prime factors to go straight to finding
the HCF, but there's a good chance of making a mistake.
It's much safer to list all the factors and find the HCF
that way, even if it takes a bit longer.

2 Multiples of 3 are: 3, 6, 9, 12, ⑮, 18, ...
Multiples of 5 are: 5, 10, ⑮, 20, ...

So it will be 15 minutes until they are side by side at the start line.
[2 marks available — 1 mark for a correct method,
1 mark for the correct answer]

3 Multiples of 35 are: 35, 70, 105, 140, 175, 210, 245, 280, 315, 350, ㉟⑤, 420, ...
Multiples of 55 are: 55, 110, 165, 220, 275, 330, ㉟⑤, 440, ...

So the LCM is 385, which is the minimum number of jars he needs.

So the minimum number of packs he needs is $385 ÷ 35 = 11$ packs
[3 marks available — 1 mark for a correct method to find LCM,
1 mark for LCM correct, 1 mark for correct number of packs]

Page 16: Fractions, Decimals and Percentages

1 a) $\dfrac{3}{4} = 3 ÷ 4 = 0.75$ *[1 mark]*

b) $0.06 × 100 = 6\%$ *[1 mark]*

c) $35\% = \dfrac{35}{100}$ *[1 mark]*
$= \dfrac{35 ÷ 5}{100 ÷ 5} = \dfrac{7}{20}$ *[1 mark]*
[2 marks available in total — as above]

2 a) $14 ÷ 20 = 0.7$ *[1 mark]*
$0.7 × 100 = 70\%$ *[1 mark]*
[2 marks available in total — as above]
Or you could multiply the top and bottom of the fraction by 5 to
give $\dfrac{70}{100} = 70\%$.

b) $85\% = \dfrac{85}{100}$ *[1 mark]*
$= \dfrac{85 ÷ 5}{100 ÷ 5} = \dfrac{17}{20}$ *[1 mark]*
[2 marks available in total — as above]

3 Convert $\dfrac{2}{5}$ to a percentage:
$2 ÷ 5 × 100 = 0.4 × 100 = 40\%$ *[1 mark]*
$100\% − (44\% + 40\%) = 100\% − 84\% = 16\%$ *[1 mark]*
So 16% of the guests have a vegetarian main course.
$100\% = 200,\ 10\% = 20,\ 1\% = 2$
$16\% = 10\% + 6\%$
$\quad = 20 + (6 × 2)$
$\quad = 20 + 12 = 32$ guests had a vegetarian main course. *[1 mark]*
[3 marks available in total — as above]

You would still get the marks if you chose to convert 44% to a
fraction, or both 44% and $\dfrac{2}{5}$ to decimals — but using percentages
is probably the quickest and easiest method here. Alternatively, you could
work out the number of guests that had chicken and the number of
guests that had salmon, and subtract from 200.

Page 17: Equivalent Fractions

1 a) $\frac{12 \div 6}{30 \div 6} = \frac{2}{5}$ *[1 mark]*

   b) 18 shaded squares out of 50, so $\frac{18}{50} = \frac{9}{25}$

   [2 marks available — 2 marks for the correct final answer, otherwise 1 mark for a correct equivalent fraction]

   c) E.g.

   [1 mark for any 40 squares shaded]

2 a) $\frac{18}{7} = 2\frac{4}{7}$ *[1 mark]*

   b) $1\frac{3}{4} = \frac{4+3}{4} = \frac{7}{4}$ *[1 mark]*

3 a) $\frac{3}{12} = \frac{1}{4} \neq \frac{1}{3}$ and $\frac{6}{20} = \frac{3}{10} \neq \frac{3}{9} = \frac{1}{3}$

   So $\frac{3}{12}$ and $\frac{6}{20}$

   [2 marks available — 1 mark for each correct answer]

   b) $\frac{4}{5} = \frac{36}{45}, \frac{7}{9} = \frac{35}{45}, \frac{13}{15} = \frac{39}{45}$

   So the largest fraction is $\frac{13}{15}$

   [3 marks available — 1 mark for attempting to convert to equivalent fractions or to draw shaded diagrams, 1 mark if these are correct, 1 mark for the correct conclusion]

Pages 18-20: Fractions

1 a) $\frac{1}{2} \times \frac{1}{6} = \frac{1 \times 1}{2 \times 6} = \frac{1}{12}$ *[1 mark]*

   b) $\frac{2}{3} \div \frac{3}{5} = \frac{2}{3} \times \frac{5}{3} = \frac{2 \times 5}{3 \times 3} = \frac{10}{9}$ or $1\frac{1}{9}$

   [2 marks available — 1 mark for changing to the reciprocal fraction and multiplying, 1 mark for the correct answer]

2 a) $\frac{3}{4} \times \frac{2}{5} = \frac{3 \times 2}{4 \times 5} = \frac{6}{20} = \frac{3}{10}$

   [2 marks available — 1 mark for multiplying the fractions, 1 mark for the final answer in its simplest form]

   b) $9)\overline{2.^20^20^20...}$ gives $0.222...$

   So $\frac{2}{9} = 0.222... = 0.\dot{2}$

   [3 marks available — 1 mark for using a division method, 1 mark for 0.22..., 1 mark for the correct final answer]

3 a) $\frac{1}{6} + \frac{2}{3} = \frac{1}{6} + \frac{4}{6} = \frac{1+4}{6} = \frac{5}{6}$

   [2 marks available — 1 mark for finding a common denominator, 1 mark for the correct answer]

   b) $\frac{7}{8} - \frac{3}{4} = \frac{7}{8} - \frac{6}{8} = \frac{7-6}{8} = \frac{1}{8}$

   [2 marks available — 1 mark for finding a common denominator, 1 mark for the correct answer]

4 a) $\frac{1}{3} + \frac{2}{5} = \frac{5}{15} + \frac{6}{15} = \frac{5+6}{15} = \frac{11}{15}$

   [2 marks available — 1 mark for finding a common denominator, 1 mark for the correct answer]

   b) $\frac{1}{2} - \frac{2}{7} = \frac{7}{14} - \frac{4}{14} = \frac{7-4}{14} = \frac{3}{14}$

   [2 marks available — 1 mark for finding a common denominator, 1 mark for the correct answer]

5 a) $(60 \div 5) \times 3 = 12 \times 3 = 36$

   [2 marks available — 1 mark for dividing by 5, 1 mark for the correct answer]

   You could also multiply 60 by 0.6.

   b) $\frac{15}{40} = \frac{3}{8}$

   [2 marks available — 1 mark for putting the numbers into a fraction, 1 mark for the correct final answer]

6 7 *[1 mark]*

7 $(12\,400 \div 8) \times 3 = 1550 \times 3 = 4650$

   [2 marks available — 1 mark for dividing by 8, 1 mark for the correct answer]

8 $1 - \frac{7}{10} = \frac{3}{10}$

   $(£9 \div 10) \times 3 = £.90 \times 3 = £23.70$

   [3 marks available — 1 mark for finding the fraction to spend on fiction books, 1 mark for dividing by 10, 1 mark for the correct answer]

9 Calculate the total cost if he pays in full today:
   £1100 ÷ 4 = £275, £1100 − £275 = £825
   Calculate the total cost if he pays £150 today, then 12 monthly payments of £55:
   £150 + (12 × £55) = £150 + £660 = £810
   So the cheaper way for Chris to pay for the car is by paying £150 today, followed by 12 monthly payments of £55.

   [4 marks available — 1 mark for the correct method to find the total cost if he pays in full today, 1 mark for the correct method to find the total cost if he pays £150 then 12 monthly payments, 1 mark if both of these values are correct, 1 mark for the correct conclusion from your values]

10 Number of acres used for wheat = (36 ÷ 12) × 5 = 3 × 5 = 15
   Number of acres used for cows = 36 ÷ 3 = 12
   Number of acres used for pigs = 36 ÷ 6 = 6 *[1 mark]*
   Cost to run per year = (15 + 12 + 6) × £400 = 33 × £400
   = £13 200 *[1 mark]*
   Income from wheat = £1100 × 15 = £16 500
   Income from cows = £1450 × 12 = £17 400
   Income from pigs = £1250 × 6 = £7500 *[1 mark]*
   Total profit = £16 500 + £17 400 + £7500 − £13 200 = £28 200
   [1 mark]
   [4 marks available in total — as above]
   Alternatively you could work out the profit from each of wheat, cows and pigs, then add them up.

Page 21: Proportion Problems

1 Price per ml:
   250 ml bottle: £2.30 ÷ 250 = £0.0092
   330 ml bottle: £2.97 ÷ 330 = £0.009
   500 ml bottle: £4.10 ÷ 500 = £0.0082
   Therefore the 500 ml bottle is the best value for money.
   [2 marks available — 1 mark for finding the price per ml, 1 mark for the correct answer]

2 Flour: (175 ÷ 20) × 70 = 612.5 g
   Butter: (175 ÷ 20) × 70 = 612.5 g
   Sugar: (120 ÷ 20) × 70 = 420 g
   Baking powder: (2.5 ÷ 20) × 70 = 8.75 tsp
   Eggs: (4 ÷ 20) × 70 = 14
   [3 marks available — 1 mark for dividing each quantity by 20, 1 mark for multiplying each of these by 70, 1 mark if all 5 final answers are correct]

Pages 22-23: Percentages

1 a) 10% = 10 ÷ 100 = 0.1
      10% of £18 = 0.1 × £18 = £1.80
      [2 marks available — 1 mark for a correct method, 1 mark for the correct answer]

   b) (£6 ÷ £24) × 100 = 0.25 × 100 = 25%
      [2 marks available — 1 mark for a correct method, 1 mark for the correct answer]

2 3% = 3 ÷ 100 = 0.03
   3% of £200 = 0.03 × £200 = £6
   4 × £6 = £24
   [3 marks available — 1 mark for a correct method to find 3% of £200, 1 mark for multiplying this by 4, 1 mark for the correct answer]

3 a) 20% = 20 ÷ 100 = 0.2
      20% of £33.25 = 0.2 × £33.25 = £6.65
      £33.25 + £6.65 = £39.90
      [3 marks available — 1 mark for a correct method to find 20% of £33.25, 1 mark for adding this to £33.25, 1 mark for the correct answer]
      You could multiply by 1.2 instead of multiplying by 0.2 and adding.

Answers

b) ($6.38 ÷ $29) × 100 = 0.22 × 100 = 22%
[2 marks available — 1 mark for a correct method,
1 mark for the correct answer]

c) £200 – £175 = £25 *[1 mark]*
(£25 ÷ £200) × 100 *[1 mark]*
= 12.5% *[1 mark]*
[3 marks available in total — as above]

4 £16 000 – £9440 = £6560 *[1 mark]*
20% = 20 ÷ 100 = 0.2
20% of £6560 = 0.2 × £6560 *[1 mark]*
= £1312 *[1 mark]*
[3 marks available in total — as above]

5 100% – (60% + 30%) = 10% *[1 mark]*
10% of the total number of elephants = 3 *[1 mark]*
Total number of elephants = (3 ÷ 10) × 100 *[1 mark]*
= 30 *[1 mark]*
[4 marks available in total — as above]

6 Total spent per computer = £50 + £20 = £70 *[1 mark]*
40% = 40 ÷ 100 = 0.4
40% of total spent on each computer = 0.4 × £70 = £28
So the selling price for the first 12 computers is:
£70 + £28 *[1 mark]*
= £98 *[1 mark]*
12 × £98 = £1176 *[1 mark]*
12% = 12 ÷ 100 = 0.12
12% of selling price = 0.12 × £98 = £11.76
So the new selling price is:
£98 – £11.76 *[1 mark]*
= £86.24 *[1 mark]*
8 × £86.24 = £689.92 *[1 mark]*
Total profit/loss = £1176 + £689.92 – (20 × £70)
= £1865.92 – £1400 = £465.92
So John made an overall profit of £465.92 *[1 mark]*
[8 marks available in total — as above]
If you've used a different method, but you've shown all your working
and got the correct final answer, give yourself full marks.

Pages 24-25: Ratios

1 ÷4 ⟨4:12 / 1:3⟩ ÷4
[1 mark]

2 a) boys : girls
= 12 : 14
= 6 : 7 *[1 mark]*

b) 25 ÷ (2 + 3) = 5 *[1 mark]*
Number of girls is 5 × 3 = 15 *[1 mark]*
[2 marks available in total — as above]

3 700 ÷ (4 + 3 + 7) = 700 ÷ 14
= 50 ml
Orange juice: 50 × 4 = 200 ml
Pineapple juice : 50 × 3 = 150 ml
Lemonade: 50 × 7 = 350 ml
[3 marks available — 1 mark for dividing 700 by the sum of the
numbers in the ratio, 1 mark for multiplying this number by each
number in the ratio, 1 mark if all three quantities are correct]

4 £160 ÷ (3 + 6 + 7) = £160 ÷ 16 *[1 mark]*
= £10
So Christine's share = £10 × 7 = £70 *[1 mark]*
[2 marks available in total — as above]

5 Money spent on heating and lighting:
(£21 000 × 2) ÷ 3 = £42 000 ÷ 3 = £14 000
Money for staff training and new exhibits:
£21 000 – £14 000 = £7000 *[1 mark]*
£7000 ÷ (2 + 5) = £7000 ÷ 7 = £1000 *[1 mark]*
So money spent on new exhibits = £1000 × 5 = £5000 *[1 mark]*
[3 marks available in total — as above]

6 Bryn scored 12 more points than Richard,
so 12 points = 7 parts – 4 parts = 3 parts
1 part = 12 ÷ 3 = 4 points
Richard's score 4 × 4 = 16 points
Bryn's score 16 + 12 = 28 points
Heather's score 16 + 5 = 21 points
[3 marks available — 1 mark for saying 3 parts = 12 points or
1 part = 4 points, 1 mark for multiplying one of the numbers in the
ratio by the points for 1 part, 1 mark for all three correct answers]

Page 26: Rounding Off and Estimating Calculations

1 a) 120 *[1 mark]*
b) 2600 *[1 mark]*
c) 500 000 *[1 mark]*

2 a) 428.6 light years *[1 mark]*
b) 430 light years *[1 mark]*

3 $\frac{4.32^2 - \sqrt{13.4}}{16.3 + 2.19}$ = 0.8113466... *[1 mark]*
= 0.811 *[1 mark]*
[2 marks available in total — as above]

4 E.g. $\frac{12.2 \times 1.86}{0.19} \approx \frac{10 \times 2}{0.2} = \frac{20}{0.2} = 100$
[3 marks available — 1 mark for rounding to suitable values,
1 mark for next calculation step, 1 mark for the correct final
answer using your values]

Page 27: Powers and Roots

1 a) $8.7^3 = 658.503$ *[1 mark]*
b) $\sqrt{2025} = 45$ *[1 mark]*

2 Since $6^2 = 36$ and $7^2 = 49$, $6 < \sqrt{42} < 7$
So, $\sqrt{42} \approx 6.5$ *[1 mark]*
You would be given the mark here for any answer which
was greater than 6 and less than 7.

3 $\frac{3^4 \times 3^7}{3^6} = \frac{3^{(4+7)}}{3^6} = \frac{3^{11}}{3^6} = 3^{(11-6)} = 3^5$
[2 marks available — 1 mark for a correct attempt at adding or
subtracting powers, 1 mark for the correct final answer]

4 a) $6^{(5-3)} = 6^2 = 36$ *[1 mark]*
b) $(2^4 \times 2^7) = 2^{(4+7)} = 2^{11}$
$(2^3 \times 2^2) = 2^{(3+2)} = 2^5$, so $(2^3 \times 2^2)^2 = (2^5)^2 = 2^{10}$
So $(2^4 \times 2^7) \div (2^3 \times 2^2)^2 = 2^{11} \div 2^{10} = 2^1 = 2$
[2 marks available — 1 mark if each bracket has been
correctly simplified, 1 mark for the correct answer]

Section Two — Algebra

Page 28: Simplifying Terms

1 a) $4p$ *[1 mark]*
b) $2m$ *[1 mark]*
c) $4p + 3r$
[2 marks available — 1 mark for 4p and 1 mark for 3r]

2 a) w^5 *[1 mark]*
b) $x^{(9-3)} = x^6$ *[1 mark]*
c) y^5 *[1 mark]*
Remember — if you're multiplying, you add the powers.

3 a) $10ab$ *[1 mark]*
b) $4pq$ *[1 mark]*
c) $x^2 + 4x$
[2 marks available — 1 mark for x^2 and 1 mark for 4x]

Page 29: Multiplying Out Brackets

1 a) $3(x - 2)$
$= (3 \times x) + (3 \times -2)$
$= 3x - 6$ *[1 mark]*
b) $x(x + 4)$
$= (x \times x) + (x \times 4)$
$= x^2 + 4x$ *[1 mark]*

2 a) $5(x + y)$
$= (5 \times x) + (5 \times y)$
$= 5x + 5y$ *[1 mark]*

b) $s(2s - 3)$
$= (s \times 2s) + (s \times -3)$
$= 2s^2 - 3s$ *[1 mark]*

c) $2a(2a + 3)$
$= (2a \times 2a) + (2a \times 3)$
$= 4a^2 + 6a$ *[1 mark]*

d) $2b - 3(b - 1)$
$= 2b + (-3 \times b) + (-3 \times -1)$
$= 2b - 3b + 3$ *[1 mark]*
$= 3 - b$ *[1 mark]*
[2 marks available in total — as above]

3 a) $3(x - 1) + 5(x + 2)$
$= (3 \times x) + (3 \times -1) + (5 \times x) + (5 \times 2)$
$= 3x - 3 + 5x + 10$ *[1 mark]*
$= 8x + 7$ *[1 mark]*
[2 marks available in total — as above]

b) $4a(a + 2b)$
$= (4a \times a) + (4a \times 2b)$
$= 4a^2 + 8ab$ *[1 mark]*

c) $9 - 3(x + 2)$
$= 9 + (-3 \times x) + (-3 \times 2)$
$= 9 - 3x - 6$ *[1 mark]*
$= 3 - 3x$ *[1 mark]*
[2 marks available in total — as above]

Page 30: Taking Out Common Factors

1 a) $6x + 3 = (3 \times 2x) + (3 \times 1) = 3(2x + 1)$ *[1 mark]*

b) $x(x + 7)$ *[1 mark]*

c) $5(5p - 3q)$ *[1 mark]*

2 $4a^2 - 24ab = 4(a^2 - 6ab)$
$= 4a(a - 6b)$
[2 marks available — 2 marks for the correct final answer, otherwise 1 mark if the expression is only partly factorised]

3 a) $7y - 21y^2 = 7(y - 3y^2)$
$= 7y(1 - 3y)$
[2 marks available — 2 marks for the correct final answer, otherwise 1 mark if the expression is only partly factorised]

b) $18t + 9t^2 = 9(2t + t^2)$
$= 9t(2 + t)$
[2 marks available — 2 marks for the correct final answer, otherwise 1 mark if the expression is only partly factorised]

4 a) $4x^2 + 6xy = 2(2x^2 + 3xy)$
$= 2x(2x + 3y)$
[2 marks available — 2 marks for the correct final answer, otherwise 1 mark if the expression is only partly factorised]

b) $2vw + 8v^2 = 2(vw + 4v^2)$
$= 2v(w + 4v)$
[2 marks available — 2 marks for the correct final answer, otherwise 1 mark if the expression is only partly factorised]

Pages 31-32: Solving Equations

1 a) $x + 3 = 12$
$x = 12 - 3 = 9$ *[1 mark]*

b) $6x = 24$
$x = 24 \div 6 = 4$ *[1 mark]*

c) $\frac{x}{5} = 4$
$x = 4 \times 5 = 20$ *[1 mark]*

2 a) $p - 11 = -7$
$p = -7 + 11 = 4$ *[1 mark]*

b) $2y - 5 = 9$
$2y = 9 + 5 = 14$ *[1 mark]*
$y = 14 \div 2 = 7$ *[1 mark]*
[2 marks available in total — as above]

c) $3z + 2 = z + 15$
$3z - z = 15 - 2$
$2z = 13$ *[1 mark]*
$z = 13 \div 2 = 6.5$ *[1 mark]*
[2 marks available in total — as above]

3 a) $3x + 5 = 14$
$3x = 14 - 5 = 9$ *[1 mark]*
$x = 9 \div 3 = 3$ *[1 mark]*
[2 marks available in total — as above]

b) $7x - 4 = 2x + 1$
$7x - 2x = 1 + 4$
$5x = 5$ *[1 mark]*
$x = 5 \div 5 = 1$ *[1 mark]*
[2 marks available in total — as above]

4 a) $40 - 3x = 17x$
$40 = 17x + 3x$
$40 = 20x$ *[1 mark]*
$x = 40 \div 20 = 2$ *[1 mark]*
[2 marks available in total — as above]

b) $2y - 5 = 3y - 12$
$-5 + 12 = 3y - 2y$ *[1 mark]*
$y = 7$ *[1 mark]*
[2 marks available in total — as above]

5 a) $3(a + 2) = 15$
$(3 \times a) + (3 \times 2) = 15$
$3a + 6 = 15$ *[1 mark]*
$3a = 15 - 6$
$3a = 9$ *[1 mark]*
$a = 9 \div 3 = 3$ *[1 mark]*
[3 marks available in total — as above]

b) $2b - 6 = 2(3b + 1)$
$2b - 6 = 6b + 2$ *[1 mark]*
$-6 - 2 = 6b - 2b$
$-8 = 4b$ *[1 mark]*
$b = -8 \div 4 = -2$ *[1 mark]*
[3 marks available in total — as above]

6 a) $9(e - 2) = 3e + 6$
$9e - 18 = 3e + 6$ *[1 mark]*
$9e - 3e = 6 + 18$
$6e = 24$ *[1 mark]*
$e = 24 \div 6 = 4$ *[1 mark]*
[3 marks available in total — as above]

b) $5(2c - 1) = 4(3c - 2)$
$10c - 5 = 12c - 8$ *[1 mark]*
$-5 + 8 = 12c - 10c$
$3 = 2c$ *[1 mark]*
$c = 3 \div 2 = 1.5$ *[1 mark]*
[3 marks available in total — as above]

Page 33: Writing Equations

1 $7x - 12 = 4x$ *[1 mark]*
$3x = 12$
$x = 4$
So Alexa's original number was 4. *[1 mark]*
[2 marks available in total — as above]

2 Perimeter of ABC = perimeter of $EFGH$
$3(x + 4) = 2(2x + 4) + 2(x - 1)$ *[1 mark]*
$(3 \times x) + (3 \times 4) = (2 \times 2x) + (2 \times 4) + (2 \times x) + (2 \times -1)$
$3x + 12 = 4x + 8 + 2x - 2$ *[1 mark]*
$3x + 12 = 6x + 6$
$3x = 6$ *[1 mark]*
$x = 2$ *[1 mark]*
[4 marks available in total — as above]

3 $(x + 15°) + (x + 60°) + 3x = 180°$ *[1 mark]*
$5x + 75° = 180°$ *[1 mark]*
$5x = 105°$
$x = 21°$ *[1 mark]*
Therefore largest angle = $x + 60° = 81°$ *[1 mark]*
[4 marks available in total — as above]

Page 34: Using Formulas

1 $Q = 7x - 3y$
   $Q = (7 \times 8) - (3 \times 7)$
   $Q = 56 - 21 = 35$
   [2 marks available — 1 mark for correct substitution of x and y, 1 mark for correct final answer]

2 $S = 4m^2 + 2.5n$
   $S = (4 \times 6.5 \times 6.5) + (2.5 \times 4)$
   $S = 169 + 10$
   $S = 179$
   [2 marks available — 1 mark for correct substitution of m and n, 1 mark for correct final answer]

3 $F = \dfrac{9C}{5} + 32$
   $F = (9 \times 35 \div 5) + 32$
   $F = 95 \,°F$
   [2 marks available — 1 mark for correct substitution of C, 1 mark for correct final answer]

4 a) $C = S + 7H$
       $C = 25 + (7 \times 13)$
       $C = 25 + 91 = 116$
       The cost will be £116.
       [2 marks available — 1 mark for correct substitution of S and H, 1 mark for correct final answer]
   b) $C = 2H + 5N$
       $C = (2 \times 3) + (5 \times 5)$
       $C = 6 + 25 = 31$
       The cost would be £31.
       [2 marks available — 1 mark for correct substitution of H and N, 1 mark for correct final answer]

Pages 35-36: Writing and Rearranging Formulas

1 a) Total cost = flat fee + (cost per day × number of days)
       $C = 300 + (50 \times d)$
       $C = 300 + 50d$
       [2 marks available — 2 marks for correct formula, otherwise 1 mark for just 300 + 50d]
   b) Substitute $d = 3$ into formula:
       $C = 300 + (50 \times 3)$
       $C = 300 + 150 = 450$
       Therefore Alex would have to pay £450.
       [2 marks available — 1 mark for substitution of d = 3 into formula, 1 mark for correct final answer]

2 a) Number of miles = (number of kilometres ÷ 8) × 5
       $m = (k \div 8) \times 5$
       $m = \dfrac{5k}{8}$
       [2 marks available — 2 marks for correct formula, otherwise 1 mark for just $\dfrac{5k}{8}$]
   b) Substitute $k = 110$ into formula:
       $m = \dfrac{5 \times 110}{8}$
       $m = 550 \div 8 = 68.75$
       Therefore 110 km = 68.75 miles.
       [2 marks available — 1 mark for substitution of k = 110 into formula, 1 mark for correct final answer]

3 a) $v + m$ *[1 mark]*
   b) Thickness of a book in mm =
       (thickness of 1 cover in mm × number of covers) +
       (thickness of 1 page in mm × number of pages)
       $t = (3 \times 2) + (0.1 \times x)$
       $t = 6 + 0.1x$
       [2 marks available — 2 marks for correct formula, otherwise 1 mark for just 6 + 0.1x]

4 a) Total cost = flat fee + (number of pieces of furniture × cost per piece of furniture)
       $A = 35 + (F \times 10)$
       $A = 35 + 10F$
       [2 marks available — 2 marks for correct formula, otherwise 1 mark for just 35 + 10F]
   b) Rearrange formula to give F in terms of A.
       $A - 35 = 10F$
       $F = \dfrac{A - 35}{10}$
       Substitute $A = 105$ into new formula to find F:
       $F = (105 - 35) \div 10 = 7$
       Therefore 7 pieces of furniture are being delivered.
       [3 marks available — 1 mark for rearranging the formula, 1 mark for substituting A = 105 into the formula, 1 mark for the correct final answer]

5 $P = (2x) + (2x + 1) + (3x - 5) + (2x + 1) + (2x) + (4x + 3)$
      $+ ((2x) + (3x - 5) + (2x)) + (4x + 3)$
   $P = 26x - 2$
   [3 marks available — 1 mark for identifying the 2 missing sides, 1 mark for adding together all the side lengths, 1 mark for simplifying the expression]
   The vertical side on the far left is the same as the one on the far right, and the length of the bottom of the shape is just the three shorter horizontal sides at the top added together.

6 a) $u = v - at$ *[1 mark]*
   b) $v - u = at$ *[1 mark]*
       $t = \dfrac{v - u}{a}$ *[1 mark]*
       [2 marks available in total — as above]

Pages 37-38: Number Patterns and Sequences

1 a) 36, 44 *[1 mark]*
   b) 23rd term = 25th term – (2 × difference between terms)
       = $196 - (2 \times 8) = 196 - 16 = 180$ *[1 mark]*
   c) All of the terms in the sequence must be a multiple of 4 (the first term is 4, and the difference between the terms is 8). *[1 mark]*
       90 isn't a multiple of 4, so it can't be the 12th term. *[1 mark]*
       [2 marks available in total — as above]
       You could also work out the 12th term and show that it's not 90.

2 a) 8, 13, 18, 23, 28, 33, 38
       Rule: add 5 each time.
       [2 marks available — 1 mark for all correct terms, 1 mark for the correct rule]
   b) 3, 6, 12, 24, 48, 96
       Rule: double the previous number each time.
       [2 marks available — 1 mark for all correct terms, 1 mark for the correct rule]

3 a)
       [1 mark]
   b) 81, because the number of triangles in the nth pattern is equal to n^2.
       [2 marks available — 1 mark for 81 and 1 mark for the correct reason]

4 a) There are 16 circles in pattern 8. *[1 mark]*
       There are 2 circles in pattern 1, 4 circles in pattern 2 and 6 circles in pattern 3 — so there are always 2n circles in the nth pattern of the sequence.
   b) E.g. number of straight lines in a pattern = number of circles – 1 *[1 mark]*
       So, number of straight lines in the pattern with 22 circles
       = $(22 \times 2) - 1 = 44 - 1 = 43$ *[1 mark]*
       [2 marks available in total — as above]

Answers

5 a)

$$2 \quad 9 \quad 16 \quad 23$$
$$+7 \quad +7 \quad +7$$

The common difference is 7, so $7n$ is in the formula.

$n =$	1	2	3	4
$7n =$	7	14	21	28
	-5	-5	-5	-5
nth term $=$	2	9	16	23

You have to subtract 5 to get to the term.
So the expression for the nth term is $7n - 5$.
*[2 marks available — 2 marks for the correct expression,
otherwise 1 mark for 7n]*

b) 30th term $= (7 \times 30) - 5 = 205$ *[1 mark]*

6

$$3 \quad 7 \quad 11 \quad 15 \quad 19$$
$$+4 \quad +4 \quad +4 \quad +4$$

The common difference is 4, so $4n$ is in the formula.

$4n =$	4	8	12	16	20
	-1	-1	-1	-1	-1
nth term $=$	3	7	11	15	19

You have to subtract 1 to get to the term.
So the expression for the nth term is $4n - 1$.
*[2 marks available — 2 marks for the correct expression,
otherwise 1 mark for 4n]*

Page 39: Trial and Improvement

1

x	$x^3 + 4x$	
2	$2^3 + (4 \times 2) = 8 + 8 = 16$	Too small
3	$3^3 + (4 \times 3) = 27 + 12 = 39$	Too big
2.5	$2.5^3 + (4 \times 2.5) = 25.625$	Too big
2.3	$2.3^3 + (4 \times 2.3) = 21.367$	Too small
2.4	$2.4^3 + (4 \times 2.4) = 23.424$	Too small
2.45	$2.45^3 + (4 \times 2.45) = 24.506...$	Too big

So the solution is between $x = 2.4$ and $x = 2.45$,
so to 1 d.p. the solution is $x = 2.4$
*[4 marks available — 1 mark for any trial between 2 and 3,
1 mark for any trial between 2.4 and 2.5 inclusive, 1 mark for a
different trial between 2.43 and 2.45 inclusive, 1 mark for the
correct final answer]*

2

x	$x^3 - 2x$	
1	$1^3 - (2 \times 1) = 1 - 2 = -1$	Too small
2	$2^3 - (2 \times 2) = 8 - 4 = 4$	Too big
1.5	$1.5^3 - (2 \times 1.5) = 0.375$	Too big
1.3	$1.3^3 - (2 \times 1.3) = -0.403$	Too small
1.4	$1.4^3 - (2 \times 1.4) = -0.056$	Too small
1.45	$1.45^3 - (2 \times 1.45) = 0.148...$	Too big

The solution is between $x = 1.4$ and $x = 1.45$,
so to 1 d.p. the solution is $x = 1.4$
*[4 marks available — 1 mark for any trial between 1 and 2,
1 mark for any trial between 1.4 and 1.5 inclusive, 1 mark for a
different trial between 1.42 and 1.45 inclusive, 1 mark for the
correct final answer]*

Page 40: Inequalities

1 $x \geq -2$ *[1 mark]*
*It's ≥ because the circle above the number line is coloured in,
so −2 is included.*

2 $-3, -2, -1, 0, 1$
*[2 marks available — 2 marks for all 5 numbers correct,
otherwise 1 mark for the correct answer with one number
missing or one number incorrect]*

3 a) $2a - 7 \leq 11$
$2a \leq 11 + 7$
$2a \leq 18$ *[1 mark]*
$a \leq 18 \div 2$
$a \leq 9$ *[1 mark]*
[2 marks available in total — as above]

b)

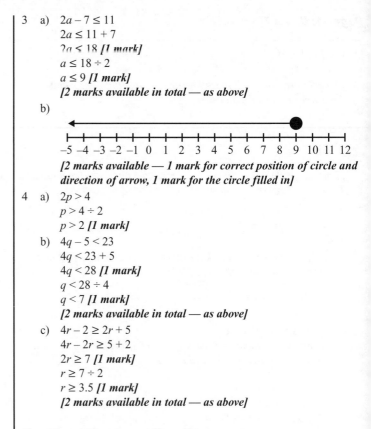

*[2 marks available — 1 mark for correct position of circle and
direction of arrow, 1 mark for the circle filled in]*

4 a) $2p > 4$
$p > 4 \div 2$
$p > 2$ *[1 mark]*

b) $4q - 5 < 23$
$4q < 23 + 5$
$4q < 28$ *[1 mark]*
$q < 28 \div 4$
$q < 7$ *[1 mark]*
[2 marks available in total — as above]

c) $4r - 2 \geq 2r + 5$
$4r - 2r \geq 5 + 2$
$2r \geq 7$ *[1 mark]*
$r \geq 7 \div 2$
$r \geq 3.5$ *[1 mark]*
[2 marks available in total — as above]

Section Three — Graphs

Pages 41-42: Coordinates and Midpoints

1 a) $(2, 1)$ *[1 mark]*

b) $(3, -2)$ *[1 mark]*

c)

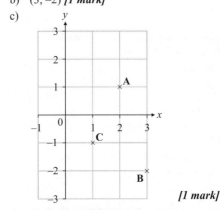

[1 mark]

2 a) $(1, 3)$ *[1 mark]*

b) $(1, 0)$ *[2 marks available — 2 marks for the correct answer,
otherwise 1 mark for correctly drawing point S on graph]*

c) $(0, 4)$ *[2 marks available — 2 marks for the correct answer,
otherwise 1 mark for correctly drawing point T on graph]*

3 a) $\left(\dfrac{1+3}{2}, \dfrac{3+(-1)}{2} \right) = (2, 1)$
*[2 marks available — 1 mark for correct method and 1 mark
for correct final answer]*
*A correct method here is to find the averages of the x- and
y-coordinates. Alternatively, you could identify the midpoint of AB
on the graph to get your answer — but the first way is much safer.*

b) $(2, -1)$ is not on the line **BC** OR the midpoint of **BC** is
actually $(2, -2)$ *[1 mark]*

4 a)

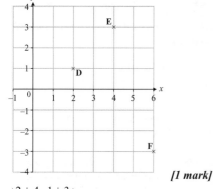

[1 mark]

b) $\left(\dfrac{2+4}{2}, \dfrac{1+3}{2}\right) = (3, 2)$

[2 marks available — 1 mark for correct method and 1 mark for correct final answer]

c) $\left(\dfrac{2+6}{2}, \dfrac{1+(-3)}{2}\right) = (4, -1)$

[2 marks available — 1 mark for correct method and 1 mark for correct final answer]

Pages 43-44: Straight-Line Graphs

1 a)

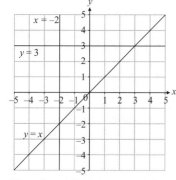

[3 marks available — 1 mark for each correct line]

b) (3, 3) *[1 mark]*

2 a)

x	−2	−1	0	1	2
y	−8	−5	−2	1	**4**

[2 marks available — 2 marks for all values correct, otherwise 1 mark for 2 correct values]

b)

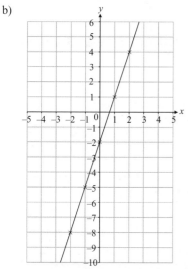

[2 marks available — 2 marks for all points plotted correctly and a straight line drawn from (−2, −8) to (2, 4), otherwise 1 mark for a correct straight line that passes through at least 3 correct points, or a straight line with the correct gradient, or a straight line with a positive gradient passing through (0, −2)]

c)

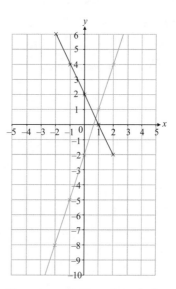

[3 marks available — 3 marks for a correct line drawn from (−2, 6) to (2, −2), otherwise 2 marks for a line that passes through (0, 2) and has a gradient of −2, or 1 mark for a line passing through (0, 2), or a line with a gradient of −2]

3 a)

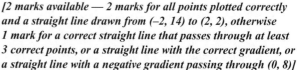

x	−2	−1	0	1	2
y	14	11	8	5	**2**

[2 marks available — 2 marks for all values correct, otherwise 1 mark for 2 correct values]

b)

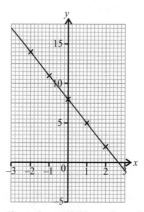

[2 marks available — 2 marks for all points plotted correctly and a straight line drawn from (−2, 14) to (2, 2), otherwise 1 mark for a correct straight line that passes through at least 3 correct points, or a straight line with the correct gradient, or a straight line with a negative gradient passing through (0, 8)]

4

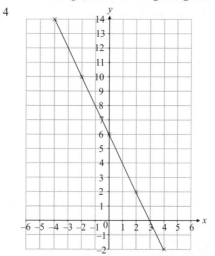

[3 marks available — 3 marks for a correct line drawn from (−4, 14) to (4, −2), otherwise 2 marks for a line that passes through (0, 6) and has a gradient of −2, or 1 mark for a line that passes through (0, 6), or a line with a gradient of −2]

Pages 45-46: Travel Graphs

1 a) $\frac{15-0}{1-0} = \frac{15}{1} = 15$ km/h

    [2 marks available — 1 mark for a correct method, 1 mark for correct final answer]

  b) The speed at which Selby was travelling. *[1 mark]*

  c) 3 hours *[1 mark]*

    As he was at point A at 0 hours, all you have to do is read off the x-value at point C to see how long Selby's journey was.

  d) 2.5 hours *[1 mark]*

  e)

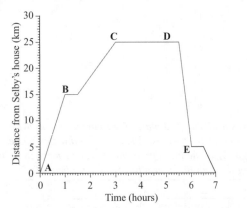

    [2 marks available — 1 mark for a flat line from point E for 30 minutes, and 1 mark for a straight line from the end of the flat line to (7, 0)]

  f) $7 - 0.5 - 2.5 - 0.5 = 3.5$ hours *[1 mark]*

    Selby isn't cycling whenever the graph shows a horizontal line. So, subtract these times from the total amount of time he is out.

2 a) 1.25 hours *[1 mark]*

  b)

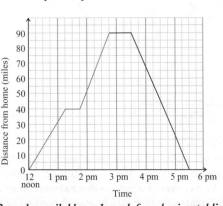

    [2 marks available — 1 mark for a horizontal line between (2.75, 90) and (3.5, 90), and 1 mark for line from (3.5, 90) to (5.5, 0) or a line parallel to this starting at the wrong point]

  c) 5 hours 30 minutes *[1 mark]*

  d) 1.45 pm and 2.45 pm *[1 mark]*

    The steeper the gradient, the faster the person is travelling. The gradient is steepest between 1.45 pm and 2.45 pm.

3 a)

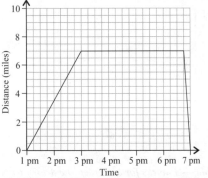

    [3 marks available — 1 mark for line from (1, 0) to (3, 7), 1 mark for horizontal line for 3 hours and 45 minutes from (3, 7), 1 mark for line from (6.75, 7) to (7, 0)]

  b) speed $= \frac{\text{distance}}{\text{time}}$, so $\frac{7}{0.25} = 28$ mph

    [2 marks available — 1 mark for a correct method, 1 mark for correct final answer]

Pages 47-48: Conversion Graphs

1 a) 36 litres (allow 35 – 37 litres) *[1 mark]*

  b) 4.5 gallons (allow 4.3 – 4.5 gallons) *[1 mark]*

  c) 40 litres = 8.8 gallons (allow 8.6 – 9.0 gallons)

    $40 \times 2 = 80$, so 8.8 gallons $\times 2 = 17.6$ gallons

    (allow 17.2 – 18.0 gallons)

    [3 marks available — 1 mark for correct conversion factor, 1 mark for correct application of the conversion factor and 1 mark for answer within the range 17.2 – 18.0]

2 a) 26 °C *[1 mark for an answer between 26 and 27 °C]*

  b) 86 °F *[1 mark for an answer between 85 and 87 °F]*

  c) $38 - 26 = 12$ °C

    [2 marks available — 1 mark for subtracting one temperature from the other, 1 mark for an answer between 10 and 12 °C]

3 Holiday spending = €50 + €70 + €100 = €220

  Home spending = £30 + £50 + £80 = £160

  Convert £160 to euros:

  From graph £4 = €5.60

  So, £40 = €56

  So, £160 = €56 × 4 = €224

  Since €224 is more than €220, Edwige is correct — she spent less than she normally would while on holiday.

  [5 marks available — 1 mark for totalling the home spending values, 1 mark for totalling the holiday spending values, 1 mark for a correct method to convert to a common currency, 1 mark for a correct conversion, 1 mark for a correct comparison]

  You could also answer this question by converting the holiday spending into pounds. Either way, as long as you convert them into the same units, you can make a comparison.

4 E.g. convert stone to lb: 1 stone = 14 lb *[1 mark]*

  so, 5.5 stone = 14 × 5.5 = 77 lb *[1 mark]*

  Convert lb to kg: 11 lb = 5 kg *[1 mark]*

  so, 77 lb = 5 × 7 = 35 kg (allow 34 – 36 kg) *[1 mark]*

  [4 marks available in total — as above]

Page 49: Real-Life Graphs

1 a) £15 *[1 mark]*

  b) 25 items *[1 mark]*

  c) $(50 \times 1) + 5 = £55$

    [2 marks available — 1 mark for a correct method, 1 mark for the correct final answer]

2 a) (i) £18 *[1 mark]*

    (ii) $40 \div 100$ *[1 mark]*

      = 0.4, so it costs 40p per unit *[1 mark]*

    [2 marks available in total — as above]

  b) Mr Barker should use Plan A because it is cheaper. Using 85 units with Plan A would cost £26.50. 85 units with Plan B would cost £34.

    [2 marks available — 1 mark for correctly stating which plan, 1 mark for giving a reason]

Page 50: Quadratic Graphs

1 a)

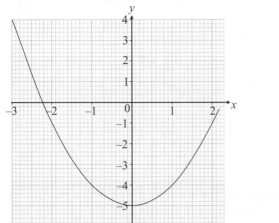

[2 marks available — 1 mark if all points are plotted correctly, 1 mark for a smooth curve joining the correctly plotted points]

b) −2.2 (allow −2.3 to −2.1) *[1 mark]*

2 a)

x	−4	−3	−2	−1	0	1	2
y	8	3	0	−1	**0**	**3**	**8**

[1 mark]

b)

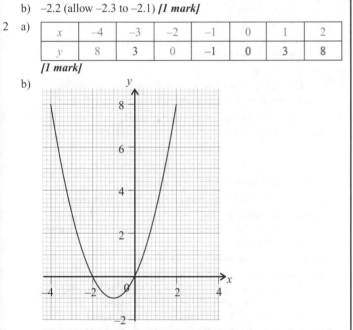

[2 marks available — 1 mark if all points are plotted correctly, 1 mark for a smooth curve joining the correctly plotted points]

c) 1.6 metres (allow 1.5 – 1.8 metres)
[2 marks available — 1 mark for indicating 6 on the y-axis, 1 mark for the correct final answer]
If the width of the pool is x and the length is (x + 2), then the area is x(x + 2), and you can use the graph to find when x(x + 2) = 6.

Section Four — Shapes and Area

Pages 51-52: Symmetry and Tessellations

1 a)

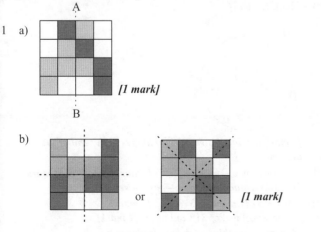

[1 mark]

b)

or *[1 mark]*

c)

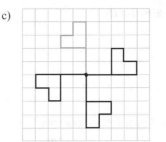

[2 marks available in total — 2 marks for the correct shape, otherwise 1 mark for drawing one of the three missing 'arms' correctly]

2 a) A and B
[2 marks available — 1 mark for each correct letter]

b) E *[1 mark]*

c)

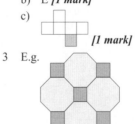
[1 mark]

3 E.g.

[2 marks available in total — 2 marks for at least four of each type of tile tessellating correctly, otherwise 1 mark for two or three of each type of tile tessellating correctly]

4 E.g.

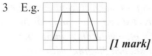

[2 marks available in total — 2 marks for four shapes correctly tessellated, otherwise 1 mark for three shapes correctly tessellated]
It's also possible to tessellate these shapes by rotating some of them.

Page 53: Properties of 2D Shapes

1 a) Isosceles triangle *[1 mark]*
You need to say "isosceles triangle" to get the mark, not just "triangle".

b) C *[1 mark]*

2 E.g.

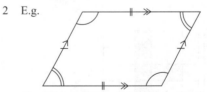

[2 marks available — 1 mark for 2 pairs of equal sides, 1 mark for 2 pairs of equal angles]
Read the information carefully — there's only one type of shape this could be.

3 E.g.

[1 mark]

There isn't just one right answer here — as long as your shape has four sides, with two of them parallel, you'll get the mark.

4 a) No lines of symmetry *[1 mark]*

b) Order 2 *[1 mark]*

Page 54: Congruence and Similarity

1

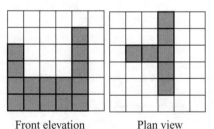

   a) *[1 mark for shapes correctly labelled 'C' — as above]*
   b) *[1 mark for shapes correctly labelled 'S' — as above]*

2 a) Triangle *AEX* *[1 mark]*
   b) Triangle *AYX* *[1 mark]*

3   A and F *[1 mark]*
    C and D *[1 mark]*
    [2 marks available in total — as above]

Page 55: 3D Shapes

1   A = Sphere *[1 mark]*
    B = Cone *[1 mark]*
    [2 marks available in total — as above]

2 a) 6 *[1 mark]*
   b) 12 *[1 mark]*
   c) 8 *[1 mark]*

3 a) Pyramid or square-based pyramid *[1 mark]*
   b) 6 *[1 mark]*
   c) B *[1 mark]*
   d) D *[1 mark]*

Page 56: Projections

1

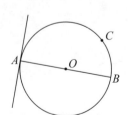

*[3 marks available — 1 mark for a width of 6 squares,
1 mark for a height of 9 squares, 1 mark for a correct dotted or
solid line marking the edge of the roof]*

2

Front elevation   Plan view

*[4 marks available in total — 2 marks for a correct front elevation
diagram, otherwise 1 mark for a correct shape with one error in
dimensions, and 2 marks for a correct plan view diagram in any
orientation, otherwise 1 mark for a T-shaped diagram with the
wrong dimensions]*

3

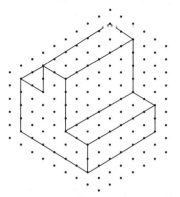

*[2 marks available in total — 2 marks for a correct diagram, other-
wise 1 mark for the correct cross-section but wrong length]*

Pages 57-58: Perimeters and Areas

1 a) 18 cm *[1 mark]*
   b) 14 cm² *[1 mark]*

2 a) 6.4 × 10 = 64 cm²
     *[2 marks available — 1 mark for correct calculation,
     1 mark for correct answer]*
   b) $\sqrt{64}$ = 8 cm
     *[2 marks available — 1 mark for correct calculation,
     1 mark for correct answer]*

3   Area of rectangle = 6 × 8 = 48 cm² *[1 mark]*
    Base of triangle = 8 cm – 5 cm = 3 cm *[1 mark]*
    Area of triangle = $\frac{1}{2}$ × 3 × 4 = 6 cm² *[1 mark]*
    Area of shaded area = 48 – 6 *[1 mark]* = 42 cm² *[1 mark]*
    [5 marks available in total — as above]

4   Area of field = ½ × (105 + 80) × 60 = 5550 m² *[1 mark]*
    Price of weedkiller per m² = 0.27 ÷ 10 = £0.027 *[1 mark]*
    Cost = area × price per square metre = 5550 × 0.027 *[1 mark]*
    = £149.85 *[1 mark]*
    [4 marks available in total — as above]

5 a) Area of patio = 5 × 5 = 25 m² *[1 mark]*
     Area of lawn and patio = 27 × 10 = 270 m² *[1 mark]*
     Area of lawn = 270 – 25 = 245 m² *[1 mark]*
     245 ÷ 10 = 24.5, so 25 boxes needed. *[1 mark]*
     Cost = no. of boxes × price per box = 25 × 7 *[1 mark]*
     = £175.00 *[1 mark]*
     [6 marks available in total — as above]
   b) Perimeter of lawn = 10 + 22 + 5 + 5 + 5 + 27 = 74 m *[1 mark]*
     No. of strips = perimeter ÷ length of strip = 74 ÷ 2 *[1 mark]*
     = 37 strips *[1 mark]*
     [3 marks available in total — as above]

Pages 59-60: Circles

1 a) Diameter *[1 mark]*
   b) Radius *[1 mark]*
   c) Chord *[1 mark]*
   d)

*[1 mark for line drawn at right angles to the end of the
diameter at A]*

2 a) Circumference = π × (2 × 0.25) *[1 mark]* = 1.57 m *[1 mark]*
     [2 marks available in total — as above]
   b) 500 ÷ 1.57 *[1 mark]* = 318.47... *[1 mark]*
     So the wheel makes 318 full turns. *[1 mark]*
     [3 marks available in total — as above]

3 a) 19.5×13 *[1 mark]* $= 253.5$ cm² *[1 mark]*
   [2 marks available in total — as above]

b) Radius of biscuit = $13 \div 4 = 3.25$ cm *[1 mark]*
   Area of biscuit = $\pi r^2 = \pi \times 3.25^2$ *[1 mark]*
   $= 33.2$ cm² (to 1 d.p.) *[1 mark]*
   [3 marks available in total — as above]

4 Area of outside circle = $\pi \times 5^2 = 78.53...$ cm² *[1 mark]*
  Area of inside circle = $\pi \times 3^2 = 28.27...$ cm² *[1 mark]*
  Area of letter "O" = $78.53... - 28.27...$ *[1 mark]*
  $= 50.3$ cm² (to 3 s.f) *[1 mark]*
  [4 marks available in total — as above]

5 Area of square = $8 \times 8 = 64$ m² *[1 mark]*
  Area of circle = $\pi \times 4^2 = 50.26...$ m² *[1 mark]*
  Area of grass = $64 - 50.26... = 13.73...$ m² *[1 mark]*
  No. of packets = $13.73... \div 0.5 = 27.469...$ *[1 mark]*
  So he will need 28 packets. *[1 mark]*
  [6 marks available in total — as above]

6 Area of cookie = $\pi \times 5^2$ *[1 mark]* $= 78.53...$ cm² *[1 mark]*
  $78.53... \div 3$ *[1 mark]* $= 26.17...$ *[1 mark]*
  So the maximum number of buttons is 26. *[1 mark]*
  [5 marks available in total — as above]

Pages 61-62: Volume

1 Area of cross-section is 7 squares and the length is 3 cubes,
  so volume = $7 \times 3 = 21$ cm³
  *[2 marks available — 1 mark for correct method,
  1 mark for correct answer]*

2 Volume = $6 \times 10 \times 14 = 840$ cm³
  *[2 marks available — 1 mark for correct calculation,
  1 mark for correct answer]*

3 Area of cross-section = $\pi \times 1^2 = 3.141...$ m² *[1 mark]*
  Volume of paddling pool = height × area of cross-section
  $= 0.4 \times 3.141...$ *[1 mark]*
  $= 1.26$ m³ (to 2 d.p.) *[1 mark]*
  [3 marks available in total — as above]

4 Area of cross-section = $\frac{1}{2} \times 6 \times 4 = 12$ cm² *[1 mark]*
  Volume of prism = 12×4 *[1 mark]* $= 48$ cm³ *[1 mark]*
  [3 marks available in total — as above]

5 a) Volume = $90 \times 40 \times 30$ *[1 mark]* $= 108\,000$ cm³ *[1 mark]*
   [2 marks available in total — as above]

b) Number of fish = $108\,000 \div 6000 = 18$
   So the greatest number of fish the tank can hold is 18.
   *[2 marks available — 1 mark for correct calculation,
   1 mark for correct answer]*

6 $40 \div 8 = 5$, so exactly 5 boxes fit into the width of each case.
  $16 \div 8 = 2$, so exactly 2 boxes fit into the height of each case.
  $50 \div 8 = 6.25$, so you can only fit 6 boxes along the length of the
  case, with a small gap at the end.
  So each case can take a maximum of $5 \times 2 \times 6 = 60$ boxes of fudge.
  *[3 marks available — 1 mark for a correct method, 1 mark for at
  least one division correct, and 1 mark for the correct final answer]*
  *You need to think practically here — if you divided the volume of the
  case by the volume of one box, you'd get 62.5. But you can't put bits of
  boxes in to fill gaps. So you need to stop and think about what the best
  way of packing whole boxes into the case is.*

Pages 63-64: Nets and Surface Area

1 E.g.

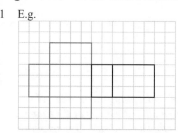

[2 marks available — 1 mark for each correctly drawn side]

2 A *[1 mark]*

3 a) E.g.

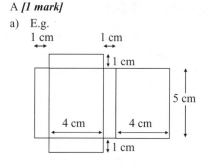

*[3 marks available in total — 3 marks for a correct and
accurately drawn diagram, otherwise 1 mark for a net of any
cuboid, or 2 marks for a net with five faces correct]*
*There are several ways to make a cuboid net, so the faces in your
net could be in different places relative to each other.*

b) Area of front = $4 \times 1 = 4$ cm²
   Area of side = $5 \times 1 = 5$ cm²
   Area of top = $4 \times 5 = 20$ cm²
   Total surface area = $2 \times (4 + 5 + 20) = 58$ cm²
   *[3 marks available — 1 mark for finding the area of each face,
   1 mark for adding the areas, 1 mark for the correct final answer]*

4

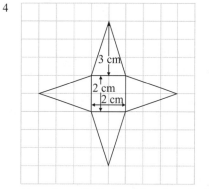

*[3 marks available in total — 3 marks for a correct and accurately
drawn diagram, otherwise 1 mark for a square and 4 triangles with
the wrong measurements, or 2 marks for a correctly-sized square
and 4 isosceles triangles with the wrong measurements]*
*There are other ways of drawing this net, but this is really the only
sensible way of doing it.*

5 Surface area = $(2 \times 2\,\text{m} \times 1\,\text{m}) + (2 \times 2\,\text{m} \times 0.03\,\text{m}) +$
  $(2 \times 1\,\text{m} \times 0.03\,\text{m}) = 4.18$ m²
  Dan needs enough varnish to cover 4.18 m² $\times 2 = 8.36$ m².
  8.36 m² $\div 2.45$ m² $= 3.4122...$ tins. So Dan should buy 4 tins.
  *[4 marks available — 1 mark for a correct method for finding the
  surface area, 1 mark for the correct surface area, 1 mark for a
  correct method for calculating the number of tins, and 1 mark for
  the correct final answer]*

  *Don't forget you need to round up here — not down. 3 tins wouldn't be
  enough, since you've worked out that Dan needs 3.4122... tins.*

6 Area of cross-section = $\pi \times 3^2 = 28.274...$ cm² *[1 mark]*
  Circumference = $\pi \times 6 = 18.849...$ cm
  Area of curved surface = circumference × length
  $= 18.849... \times 11 = 207.345...$ cm² *[1 mark]*
  Total surface area = $(2 \times 28.274...) + 207.345...$ *[1 mark]*
  $= 264$ cm² (to 3 s.f.) *[1 mark]*
  [4 marks available in total — as above]
  *The area of the curved surface is the circumference × the length
  because the length of the edge that meets the circle is the same length
  as the circle's circumference.*

Section Five — Angles and Geometry

Pages 65-66: Measuring and Drawing Lines and Angles

1 a) 11 cm *[1 mark, allow ± 1 mm]*

   b) A———————————✗———————————B *[1 mark]*
   Measure to check your cross is 5.5 cm from either end.

2 a)
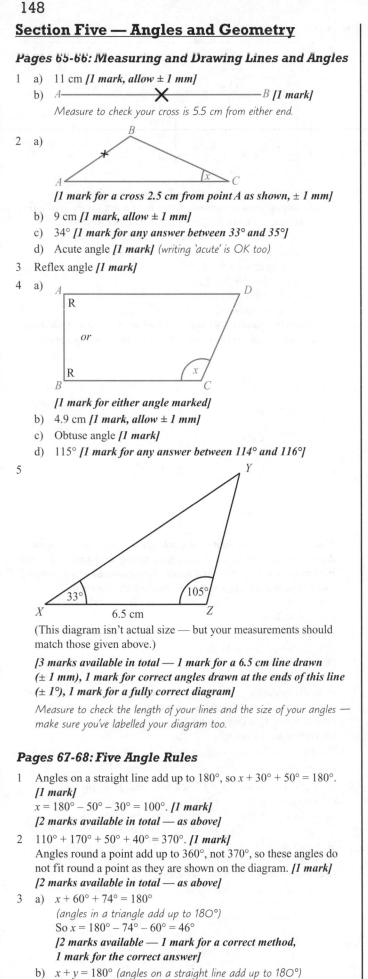
   [1 mark for a cross 2.5 cm from point A as shown, ± 1 mm]

   b) 9 cm *[1 mark, allow ± 1 mm]*

   c) 34° *[1 mark for any answer between 33° and 35°]*

   d) Acute angle *[1 mark]* (writing 'acute' is OK too)

3 Reflex angle *[1 mark]*

4 a)

   [1 mark for either angle marked]

   b) 4.9 cm *[1 mark, allow ± 1 mm]*

   c) Obtuse angle *[1 mark]*

   d) 115° *[1 mark for any answer between 114° and 116°]*

5

   (This diagram isn't actual size — but your measurements should match those given above.)

   [3 marks available in total — 1 mark for a 6.5 cm line drawn (± 1 mm), 1 mark for correct angles drawn at the ends of this line (± 1°), 1 mark for a fully correct diagram]

   Measure to check the length of your lines and the size of your angles — make sure you've labelled your diagram too.

Pages 67-68: Five Angle Rules

1 Angles on a straight line add up to 180°, so $x + 30° + 50° = 180°$.
   [1 mark]
   $x = 180° - 50° - 30° = 100°$. *[1 mark]*
   [2 marks available in total — as above]

2 $110° + 170° + 50° + 40° = 370°$. *[1 mark]*
   Angles round a point add up to 360°, not 370°, so these angles do not fit round a point as they are shown on the diagram. *[1 mark]*
   [2 marks available in total — as above]

3 a) $x + 60° + 74° = 180°$
      (angles in a triangle add up to 180°)
      So $x = 180° - 74° - 60° = 46°$
      [2 marks available — 1 mark for a correct method, 1 mark for the correct answer]

   b) $x + y = 180°$ *(angles on a straight line add up to 180°)*
      $46° + y = 180°$, so $y = 180° - 46° = 134°$
      [2 marks available — 1 mark for a correct method, 1 mark for the correct answer]

4 $70° + 90° + 97° = 257°$
   Angle $ADC = 360° - 257° = 103°$
   (angles in a quadrilateral add up to 360°)
   [2 marks available — 1 mark for a correct method, 1 mark for the correct answer]

5 $180° - 48° = 132°$ = Angles $ACB + BAC$ *[1 mark]*
   (angles in a triangle add up to 180°)
   Angle $ACB = 132° ÷ 2 = 66°$ *[1 mark]* (ABC is isosceles)
   Angle $BCD = 180° - 66° = 114°$ *[1 mark]*
   (angles on a straight line add up to 180°)
   [3 marks available in total — as above]

6 Angle $CBE = 180° - 115° = 65°$ *[1 mark]*
   Angle $BED = 180° - 103° = 77°$ *[1 mark]*
   because angles on a straight line add up to 180°. *[1 mark]*
   Angles in a quadrilateral add up to 360° *[1 mark]* so:
   $$x + 90° + 77° + 65° = 360°$$ (CDE is a right angle)
   $$x + 232° = 360°$$
   $$x = 360° - 232° = 128°$$ *[1 mark]*
   [5 marks available in total — as above]
   Make sure you've answered this one in clear sentences, since you're marked on the quality of your written communication.

7 Angles in a triangle add up to 180°. $180° - 96° = 84°$, *[1 mark]* so angle $VYX = 84° ÷ 2 = 42°$, because isosceles triangles have 2 equal angles. *[1 mark]* Angles on a straight line add up to 180°, so angle $UYZ = 180° - 90° - 42°$ *[1 mark]* $= 48°$ *[1 mark]*
   [4 marks available in total — as above]

Page 69: Parallel Lines

1 a)
   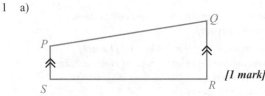
   [1 mark]

   b) Line SR *[1 mark]*

2 $a = 75°$ *[1 mark]* because vertically opposite angles are equal. *[1 mark]*
   [2 marks available in total — as above]

3 Angle $JBC = 35°$ *(vertically opposite angles)*
   Angle $BCK = 150°$ *(corresponding angles)*
   Angle $BCJ = 180° - 150° = 30°$ *[1 mark]*
   (angles on a straight line add up to 180°)
   $x° = 180° - (35° + 30°)$ *[1 mark]* $= 115°$ *[1 mark]*
   (angles in a triangle add up to 180°)
   [3 marks available in total — as above]

4 Angle $BDE = 117°$ *(corresponding angles)*
   Angle $CED = 30°$ *(vertically opposite angles)*
   Angle CDE = Angle $CED = 30°$ *[1 mark]* *(isosceles triangle)*
   x = Angle BDE − Angle CDE *[1 mark]*
   $= 117° - 30° = 87°$ *[1 mark]*
   [3 marks available in total — as above]
   There are other ways to find x. For instance, angle CBD = 180° − 117° = 63° (angles on a straight line), angle BCD = CDE (alternate angles) = 30° (see above), so x = 180° − 63° − 30° = 87° (angles in a triangle).

Page 70: Polygons, Angles and Tessellation

1 a) 7 *[1 mark]*

   b) Octagon *[1 mark]*

2 Exterior angle of a pentagon $= 360° ÷ 5 = 72°$
   Interior angle of a pentagon $= 180° - 72° = 108°$
   Angle in an equilateral triangle $= 180° ÷ 3 = 60°$
   $p = 360° - (108° + 60°)$ *(angles round a point add up to 360°)*
   $= 360° - 168° = 192°$
   [4 marks available — 1 mark for calculating the interior angle of the pentagon, 1 mark for calculating the angle of the triangle, 1 mark for using the 'angles around a point rule', 1 mark for the correct final answer]

3 a) Exterior angle = 360° ÷ 6 = 60° *[1 mark]*
Interior angle = 180° − 60° = 120° *[1 mark]*
[2 marks available in total — as above]

b) Each angle in an equilateral triangle is 60°.
The interior angle of a regular hexagon is 120°.
Angles round a point add up to 360°. *[1 mark]*
60° + 60° + 120° + 120° = 360°, *[1 mark]*
so 2 regular hexagons and 2 equilateral triangles can meet at a point. *[1 mark]*
[3 marks available in total — as above]

Pages 71-73: Transformations

1

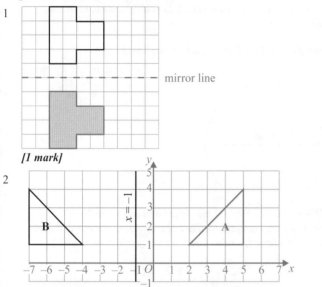

mirror line

[1 mark]

2

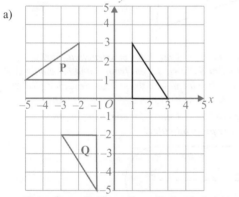

[2 marks available — 2 marks for correct reflection, otherwise 1 mark for triangle reflected but in wrong position]

3 a)

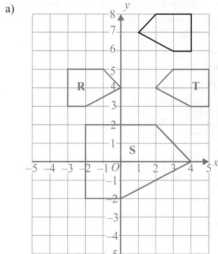

[3 marks available — 3 marks for the correct rotation, otherwise 2 marks for a correct rotation but from the wrong centre, or 1 mark for 2 points correctly rotated]

b) Rotation *[1 mark]* 90° anticlockwise *[1 mark]*
about the origin *[1 mark]*
[3 marks available in total — as above]

4 a) Translation *[1 mark]* by the vector $\begin{pmatrix} 1 \\ -7 \end{pmatrix}$ *[1 mark]*.

[2 marks available in total — as above, or with the vector described in words]

b)

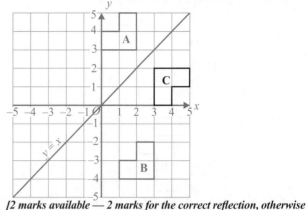

[2 marks available — 2 marks for the correct reflection, otherwise 1 mark for the correctly reflected shape in the wrong position]

c) Rotation *[1 mark]* of 180° *[1 mark]* about the point (3, −1) *[1 mark]*
[3 marks available in total — as above]

5 a)

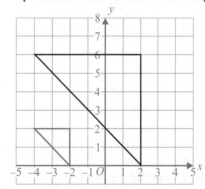

[1 mark]

b) Reflection *[1 mark]* in the line x = 1 *[1 mark]*.
[2 marks available in total — as above]

c) Enlargement *[1 mark]* of scale factor 2 *[1 mark]*,
centre (−4, 8) *[1 mark]*.
[3 marks available in total — as above]

6

[3 marks available — 3 marks for correct enlargement, otherwise 2 marks for a correct triangle but in the wrong position or for an enlargement from the correct centre but of the wrong scale factor, or 1 mark for 2 lines enlarged by the correct scale factor anywhere on the grid]

7   Reflection in the *y*-axis / in the line *x* = 0.

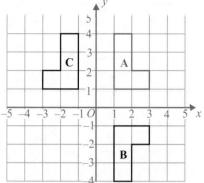

[4 marks available — 1 mark for correct position of B, 1 mark for correct position of C, 1 mark for reflection, 1 mark for mirror line]

Page 74: Similar Shape Problems

1   6 ÷ 2 = 3, scale factor 3. *[1 mark for '3']*
You can use any of the dimensions of the shape to work out the scale factor. Here, the side that's vertical on the grid is your best bet because it's the easiest length to count.

2   a)   Scale factor = 60 ÷ 24 *[1 mark]* = 2.5 *[1 mark]*
[2 marks available in total — as above]

b)   *x* = 18 × 2.5 = 45 *[1 mark]*

3

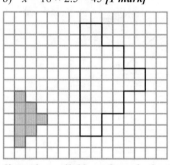

[2 marks available — 2 marks for the correct shape anywhere on the grid, pointing in any direction, otherwise 1 mark for a correct enlargement by a scale factor that's greater than 2, or 1 mark for 2 sides correct but others incorrect]

Page 75: Triangle Construction

For these questions measure your construction to check it's accurately drawn.

1

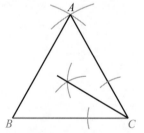

a)   *[1 mark for correct arcs at point A with straight lines joining B and C to the point where they cross]*

b)   *[2 marks available — 1 mark for compass arcs, 1 mark for bisector accurately drawn]*

2

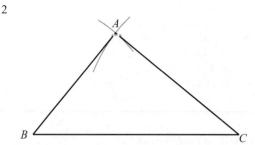

[3 marks available — 1 mark for BC within 1 mm of 5.6 cm, 1 mark for AB within 1 mm of 3.5 cm if correct construction arc is shown, 1 mark for AC within 1 mm of 4.3 cm if correct construction arc is shown]

Pages 76-77: Loci and Constructions

For these questions measure your diagram to check it's accurately drawn.

1

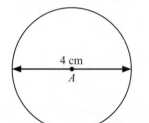

[2 marks available — 2 marks for an accurately drawn circle with a diameter within 1 mm of 6 cm, otherwise 1 mark for an accurately drawn circle with any other diameter]

2

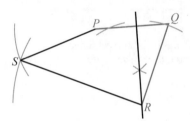

a)   *[2 marks available — 1 mark for construction marks, 1 mark for point S drawn 4.2 cm from P and 6.7 cm from R]*
Be as accurate as you can with the measurements, but you'll still get the marks if you are within 1 mm of the above lengths.

b)   *[2 marks available — 1 mark for construction arcs, 1 mark for the perpendicular]*

3

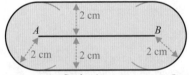

Scale: 1 cm represents 5 m
(diagram not actual size)
[2 marks available — 2 marks for arcs with a radius of 2 cm centred at A and B, lines 2 cm either side of AB and correct area shaded, otherwise 1 mark for arcs with a radius of 2 cm centred at A and B or for lines 2 cm either side of AB]
You'll still get the marks if you are within 1 mm of the correct measurements.

Answers

4

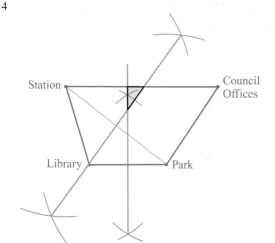

[5 marks available — 1 mark for each pair of correct arcs (centred at Library and Park and at Station and Park), 1 mark for each correct perpendicular bisector (of line between Library and Park and line between Station and Park), 1 mark for correct shaded area]

5

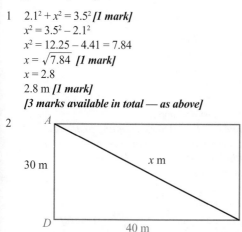

[4 marks available — 1 mark for arcs with radius of 1 cm centred at B and C, 1 mark for a line 1 cm from BC , 1 mark for an arc with radius of 2 cm centred at F, 1 mark for correct crosses at the intersections]

Page 78: Pythagoras' Theorem

1   $2.1^2 + x^2 = 3.5^2$ *[1 mark]*
   $x^2 = 3.5^2 - 2.1^2$
   $x^2 = 12.25 - 4.41 = 7.84$
   $x = \sqrt{7.84}$ *[1 mark]*
   $x = 2.8$
   2.8 m *[1 mark]*
   [3 marks available in total — as above]

2

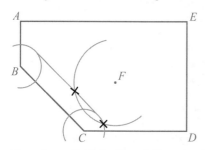

The garden is a rectangle, so the side AD is also 30 m.
The distance round the edge from A to C is 30 m + 40 m = 70 m.
[1 mark]
Let the distance across the diagonal from point A to point C be x m.
By Pythagoras' theorem $30^2 + 40^2 = x^2$ *[1 mark]*
$x = \sqrt{900 + 1600} = \sqrt{2500} = 50$ m *[1 mark]*
The price for laying the pipe across the diagonal is £8.35 per metre plus the cost of digging the trench and replacing the grass:
   £202.50 + (50 × £8.35) = £620.00 *[1 mark]*
The price for laying the pipe around the edge is £8.35 per metre:
   70 × £8.35 = £584.50 *[1 mark]*

It is cheaper to lay the pipe round the edge — it will cost £620.00 to lay the pipe across the diagonal and only £584.50 to lay it around the edge.
[1 mark for concluding that it's cheaper to lay the pipe round the edge, if the cost of each has been worked out above]
[6 marks available in total — as above]
Alternatively, instead of working out the cost of each option, you could work out the cost of the extra 20 m of pipe needed to go around the edge of the field, and show that this is less than the cost of digging a trench.

Section Six — Measures

Pages 79-80: Units and Conversions

1   a)

	Imperial	Metric
Length of a skirt	inches	centimetres
Weight of a rabbit	pounds	kilograms
Volume of a milk jug	pints	litres

[3 marks available — 1 mark for each correct answer]
   b)   8.87 m *[1 mark]*
   c)   1300 g *[1 mark]*

2   2.5 litres × 1000 = 2500 ml
   2500 ÷ 250 = 10 cups
   [3 marks available — 1 mark for converting litres to ml, 1 mark for dividing by 250, and 1 mark for final answer]
   A correct method here could also be to convert 250 ml into litres (0.25 litres) and then divide 2.5 by 0.25.

3   2500 g ÷ 1000 = 2.5 kg *[1 mark]*
   Convert kg into lb: 2.5 × 2.2 = 5.5 lb *[1 mark]*
   5.5 ÷ 1.5 = 3.6666... *[1 mark]*
   Maximum number of books = 3 *[1 mark]*
   [4 marks available in total — as above]

4   a)   40 km into miles = $\dfrac{5 \times 40}{8}$ *[1 mark]*
            = 25 miles *[1 mark]*
      [2 marks available in total — as above]

   b)   60 km/h into mph = $\dfrac{5 \times 60}{8}$ = 37.5 mph *[1 mark]*
      Since 37.5 mph is less than 40 mph, the camel would outrun a giraffe. *[1 mark]*
      [2 marks available in total — as above]

5   14 pints into litres: 14 ÷ 1.75 = 8 litres *[1 mark]*
   = 8000 ml *[1 mark]*
   (3 × 720 ml) + (5 × 520 ml) = 4760 ml *[1 mark]*
   8000 ml – 4760 ml = 3240 ml left *[1 mark]*
   3240 ÷ 540 = 6 times *[1 mark]*
   [5 marks available in total — as above]

6   39 200 ÷ 100 = 392
   392 ÷ 100 = 3.92 m²
   [2 marks available — 1 mark for correct method and 1 mark for correct final answer]
   When the unit is squared, you have to use the conversion factor twice (so you use 100, and then 100 again). You could also divide 39 200 by 10 000 instead.

Page 81: Reading Scales

1   a)   5 °C *[1 mark]*
   b)   78 mph *[1 mark]*
   c)   15 oz *[1 mark]*
2   a)   55 ml *[1 mark]*
   b)   55 – 15 *[1 mark]*
      = 40 ml *[1 mark]*
      [2 marks available in total — as above]

3 a) 40.6 m *[1 mark]*

b)

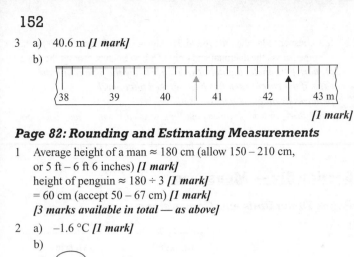

[1 mark]

Page 82: Rounding and Estimating Measurements

1 Average height of a man ≈ 180 cm (allow 150 – 210 cm, or 5 ft – 6 ft 6 inches) *[1 mark]*
height of penguin ≈ 180 ÷ 3 *[1 mark]*
= 60 cm (accept 50 – 67 cm) *[1 mark]*
[3 marks available in total — as above]

2 a) –1.6 °C *[1 mark]*

b)

[1 mark]

c) 2.5 °C *[1 mark]*

3 Minimum weight = 56.5 kg *[1 mark]*
Maximum weight = 57.5 kg *[1 mark]*
[2 marks available in total — as above]

Pages 83-84: Reading Timetables

1 a) 11:15 am *[1 mark]*

b)

[1 mark]

2 9:55 am + 2 h 15 mins *[1 mark]*
= 12:10 pm *[1 mark]*
[2 marks available in total — as above]

3 a) 17 04 *[1 mark]*

b) 6 minutes *[1 mark]*

c) 16 40 → 18 15 *[1 mark]*
= 1 h 35 mins *[1 mark]*
[2 marks available in total — as above]

4 a) 11 15 – 25 min *[1 mark]*
= 10 50 *[1 mark]*
[2 marks available in total — as above]

b) 11 35 → 13 22 = 1 h 47 min *[1 mark]*
= 107 minutes *[1 mark]*
[2 marks available in total — as above]

5 20 + 15 + 10 = 45 min *[1 mark]*
09 55 – 45 *[1 mark]*
= 09 10 *[1 mark]*
[3 marks available in total — as above, or for correctly subtracting each time in turn]

6 20 minutes + (10 × 14) = 160 minutes in total *[1 mark]*
= 160 minutes ÷ 60 = 2 hours 40 minutes *[1 mark]*
Time finished = 14 55 + 2 hours 40 minutes *[1 mark]*
= 17 35 *[1 mark]*
[4 marks available in total — as above]

Page 85: Compass Directions and Bearings

1 a) Loop the Loop *[1 mark]*

b) Dragon Train *[1 mark]*

c) south-west *[1 mark]*

2 a) 035° (accept 034° – 036°) *[1 mark]*

b)

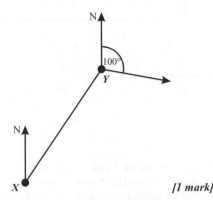

[1 mark]

Page 86: Maps and Scale Drawings

1 a) Drawing of dining table is 4 cm long.
So 4 cm is equivalent to 2 m.
2 ÷ 4 = 0.5
Therefore scale is 1 cm to 0.5 m *[1 mark]*

b) On drawing, dining table is 3 cm from shelves.
So real distance = 3 × 0.5 = 1.5 m *[1 mark]*

c) Length of drawing of room = 10 cm
So length of real room = 10 × 0.5 = 5 m *[1 mark]*
Width of drawing of room = 6 cm
So width of real room = 6 × 0.5 = 3 m *[1 mark]*
Area of room = 5 m × 3 m = 15 m² *[1 mark]*
[3 marks available in total — as above]

2 a) 4 × 2 = 8 km (allow 7.6 – 8.4 km) *[1 mark]*

b) 7 ÷ 2 = 3.5 cm *[1 mark]*

Page 87: Speed

1 speed = $\frac{\text{distance}}{\text{time}}$, so speed × time = distance *[1 mark]*
= 56 × 1.25 = 70 km *[1 mark]*
[2 marks available in total — as above]

2 a) Friday: speed = 5 ÷ 0.75 = 6.66... mph
Saturday: speed = 26 ÷ 3.25 = 8 mph
Sunday: speed = 33 ÷ 3.75 = 8.8 mph
so, Beatrix rode fastest on Sunday
[4 marks available — 1 mark for attempting to divide a distance by a time, 1 mark for getting one speed correct, 1 mark for getting the other two speeds correct, 1 mark for a correct final answer]

b) Overall speed = $\frac{\text{distance}}{\text{time}}$ *[1 mark]*
= $\frac{5 + 26 + 33}{0.75 + 3.25 + 3.75} = \frac{64}{7.75}$ *[1 mark]*
= 8.3 mph (1 dp) *[1 mark]*
[3 marks available in total — as above]

Section Seven — Statistics and Probability

Pages 88-89: Collecting Data

1 a) E.g. How many different after-school activities do you attend each week?

0	1 – 2	3 – 4	5 or more
☐	☐	☐	☐

[2 marks available — 1 mark for an appropriate question, 1 mark for at least 3 boxes which don't overlap and which cover all possible answers]

b) E.g. The results of her survey are likely to be biased as she is only asking people who attend an after-school activity. *[1 mark]*
The key idea here is "bias" — the results of her survey are likely to be an unfair representation of what all pupils at the school do.

2 a) E.g. No time frame is specified, so the response boxes are vague and could be interpreted differently by different people / the response boxes do not cover all possible answers.
[1 mark]

b) E.g. The results of his survey are likely to be biased as he is only asking boys who like football.
[1 mark]

c) E.g. Mike could assign a number to each person in his year group, generate a list of random numbers using a calculator/computer/random number table and match these two sets of numbers up to create the sample.
[2 marks available — 2 marks for a complete answer, otherwise 1 mark for mentioning a random number selection method]

3 E.g. No time frame is given. / The response boxes do not cover all possible outcomes. / The response boxes overlap.
[2 marks available — 1 mark for each of the above, up to a maximum of 2]

4 a) E.g.

How often?	Tally	Frequency
Never		
Less than once a month		
1 – 3 times a month		
4 – 6 times a month		
7 or more times a month		

[3 marks available — 1 mark for appropriate options, 1 mark for a tally column, 1 mark for a frequency or total column]

b) E.g. It leads people to say the centre does need improving.
[1 mark]

c) E.g. Do you think any of the facilities need improving?

Yes ☐   No ☐   Don't know ☐

[2 marks available — 1 mark for an appropriate question and 1 mark for appropriate answer boxes]

d) E.g. The results are likely to be biased as she will only get the views of people who already use the leisure centre.
[1 mark]

Page 90: Mean, Median, Mode and Range

1 a) In ascending order: 3, 10, 12, 12, 13, 18, 25, 33, 37, 41
Median = (13 + 18) ÷ 2 = 15.5 minutes
[2 marks available — 1 mark for ordering the numbers in ascending or descending order and 1 mark for correctly working out the median]

b) Mean = (3 + 10 + 12 + 12 + 13 + 18 + 25 + 33 + 37 + 41) ÷ 10
= 204 ÷ 10 *[1 mark]* = 20.4 minutes
= 20 minutes (to the nearest minute) *[1 mark]*
[2 marks available in total — as above]

c) Range = 41 – 3 *[1 mark]* = 38 minutes *[1 mark]*
[2 marks available in total — as above]

2 a) £18 000 *[1 mark]*

b) £18 000 *[1 mark]*

c) Mean for Company A
= (18 000 + 18 000 + 18 000 + 25 200 + 38 500) ÷ 5
= 117 700 ÷ 5 *[1 mark]* = £23 540 *[1 mark]*, so Company A has a lower mean annual salary than Company B. *[1 mark]*
[3 marks available in total — as above]

3 1, 4, 7
[2 marks available — 2 marks for all three numbers correct, otherwise 1 mark for 3 numbers that have a range of 6 and a mean of 4 but aren't all different, or 3 different numbers that add up to 12 or that have a range of 6]

Page 91: Tables

1 a) The Ivy *[1 mark]*

b) 2 *[1 mark]*

2 Cost in June = 2 × £300 + 3 × £290 = £1470
Cost in July = 2 × £330 + 3 × £275 = £1485
So it would be cheaper for the Whites to go for a week in June.
[4 marks available — 1 mark for multiplying by 2 for the adult price and by 3 for the child price, 1 mark for using the correct adult and child prices from the table, 1 mark for the correct total cost in June and the correct total cost in July, 1 mark for clearly stating that June is cheaper]

Page 92: Pictograms

1 a) 40 *[1 mark]*

b)

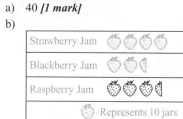

[1 mark]

c) 40 + 25+ 35 = 100 *[1 mark]*

2 a) 30 *[1 mark]*

b) 40 – 20 = 20 *[1 mark]*

c)

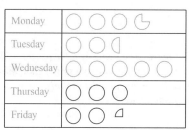

[2 marks available — 1 mark for three full circles drawn for Thursday and 1 mark for two and a quarter circles drawn for Friday]

Page 93: Bar Charts

1 a) 25 *[1 mark]*

b) Tuesday *[1 mark]*

c)

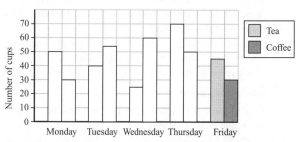

[2 marks available — 1 mark for a light shaded bar drawn to 45 and 1 mark for a dark shaded bar drawn to 30]

d) No. of cups of tea sold = 50 + 40 + 25 + 70 + 45 = 230
No. of cups of coffee sold = 30 + 55 + 60 + 50 + 30 = 225
So, there were more cups of tea sold in total.
[2 marks available — 1 mark for finding both totals, 1 mark for the correct answer]

2

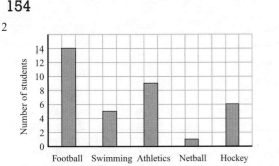

[3 marks available — 1 mark for a suitable scale, 1 mark for a fully labelled bar chart, 1 mark for all bar heights correct]

Page 94: Two-Way Tables

1 a) $200 - 140 = 60$ *[1 mark]*
   b) $23 - 9 = 14$ *[1 mark]*
   c) $200 - 23 = 177$ *[1 mark]*
       Ratio = 23:177 *[1 mark]*
       [2 marks available in total — as above]
   d) $\frac{14}{140}$ *[1 mark]* $= \frac{1}{10}$ *[1 mark]*
       [2 marks available in total — as above]

2 14 girls took part in swimming.

	Girls	Boys	Total
Swimming	**14**	10	**24**
Athletics	32	**18**	**50**
Football	**6**	35	41
Total	**52**	63	115

[4 marks available — 1 mark for a two-way table (or for a list of at least 2 combinations), 1 mark for attempting to find a missing value, 1 mark for correctly finding at least two missing values, and 1 mark for the correct final answer]

Although you don't need to work out all of the values in the table, doing so is a handy way to check your answer.

Page 95: Pie Charts

1 a) $\frac{1}{4}$ *[1 mark]*
   b) Badminton = $360 - 180 - 90 - 30 = 60°$
       Football = 180°, so 60 people = 180°
       1 person = $180° \div 60 = 3°$
       So number of people who prefer badminton = $60° \div 3° = 20$
       [2 marks available — 1 mark for a correct method, 1 mark for the correct final answer]

       There are other ways to work this out — e.g. you could also use the number of people who prefer football (60) to work out the total people surveyed and then use the angle of the badminton sector to work out what fraction of the total this is $\left(\frac{1}{6}\right)$.

2 a) Total number of people = $12 + 18 + 9 + 21 = 60$
       Multiplier = $360 \div 60 = 6$
       Plain: $12 \times 6 = 72°$
       Salted: $18 \times 6 = 108°$
       Sugared: $9 \times 6 = 54°$
       Toffee: $21 \times 6 = 126°$

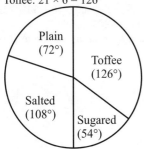

[3 marks available — 1 mark for a correct method, 1 mark for all angles drawn correctly ± 1°, 1 mark for correct labels]

b) E.g. Chris is not right because there is no information about the number of people in the ice-cream survey. *[1 mark]*

Page 96: Scatter Graphs

1 a) positive *[1 mark]*
   b) E.g.

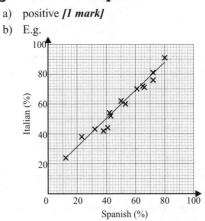

[1 mark for line of best fit that lies between (12, 16) and (12, 28) and also between (80, 82) and (80, 96)]

   c) 56%
       [2 marks available — 1 mark for indicating 66 on the y-axis, 1 mark for the x-coordinate of the line of best fit when y = 66]

2 a)

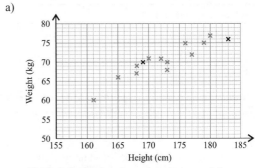

[1 mark for both points plotted correctly]

   b) E.g. In general, as the height increases, the weight also increases.
       [1 mark for any answer indicating a positive correlation]

   c) 72-74 kg
       [2 marks available — 1 mark for line of best fit, 1 mark for an answer in the range 72-74 kg]

Page 97: Stem and Leaf Diagrams

1 a) Median = $(29 + 30) \div 2 = 29.5$ mm *[1 mark]*
   b) Range = $43 - 8 = 35$ mm *[1 mark]*
   c) E.g. The rainfall was much higher in June, as the median was 15.5 mm higher. The amount of rainfall in June was more varied than in November as the range was higher in June.
       [2 marks available — 1 mark for a correct statement comparing the two medians, 1 mark for a correct statement comparing the two ranges]

2 a)
```
14 | 8
15 | 5 8 9 9
16 | 0 2 3 3 4 5 7 9 9 9
17 | 0 1 2 3 5
```
       Key: 16|2 means 162 cm

       [3 marks available — 3 marks for a fully correct diagram with a key, otherwise 1 mark for a correct key, and 1 mark for a complete diagram but with the numbers within the 'leaves' in the wrong order]

   b) Modal height = 169 cm *[1 mark]*
   c) Number of students less than 165 cm tall = 10 *[1 mark]*

Page 98: Frequency Tables and Averages

1 a)

Drink	Tally	Frequency
Cola	ⅢⅡ	7
Orange juice	Ⅲ	5
Lemonade	|||	3
Other	Ⅲ	5

[2 marks available — 2 marks if all the frequencies are correct, otherwise 1 mark if at least 2 frequencies are correct]

b) Cola *[1 mark]*

2 a) Total number of vehicles = 13 + 8 + 6 + 2 + 1 = 30, so the median is halfway between the 15th and 16th values *[1 mark]*, so the median = 1 *[1 mark]*
[2 marks available in total — as above]

b) $((13 \times 0) + (8 \times 1) + (6 \times 2) + (2 \times 3) + (1 \times 4)) \div 30$
$= (0 + 8 + 12 + 6 + 4) \div 30$
$= 30 \div 30 = 1$
[3 marks available — 1 mark for multiplying the vehicles per minute by the frequency and adding, 1 mark for dividing by 30, 1 mark for the correct final answer]

Page 99: Grouped Frequency Tables — Averages

1

Arm Span, x cm	Frequency	Mid-Interval Value	Frequency × Mid-Interval Value
$120 \leq x < 130$	13	$(120 + 130) \div 2 = 125$	$13 \times 125 = 1625$
$130 \leq x < 140$	6	$(130 + 140) \div 2 = 135$	$6 \times 135 = 810$
$140 \leq x < 150$	4	$(140 + 150) \div 2 = 145$	$4 \times 145 = 580$
$150 \leq x < 160$	7	$(150 + 160) \div 2 = 155$	$7 \times 155 = 1085$
Total	30		$1625 + 810 + 580 + 1085 = 4100$

So an estimate of the mean arm span is 4100 ÷ 30 = 136.6666...
= 137 cm (to the nearest cm.)
[4 marks available — 1 mark for the correct midpoints, 1 mark for using these to find frequency × mid-interval value, 1 mark for 4100 ÷ 30, 1 mark for the correct final answer]

2 a) Total number of children = 3 + 2 + 12 + 8 + 5 = 30, so the median value is halfway between the 15th and 16th values *[1 mark]*, so it is in the $9.5 \leq x < 10$ group *[1 mark]*
[2 marks available in total — as above]

b) $9.5 \leq x < 10$ *[1 mark]*

c)

Length of line, x cm	Frequency	Mid-Interval Value	Frequency × Mid-Interval Value
$8.5 \leq x < 9$	3	$(8.5 + 9) \div 2 = 8.75$	$3 \times 8.75 = 26.25$
$9 \leq x < 9.5$	2	$(9 + 9.5) \div 2 = 9.25$	$2 \times 9.25 = 18.5$
$9.5 \leq x < 10$	12	$(9.5 + 10) \div 2 = 9.75$	$12 \times 9.75 = 117$
$10 \leq x < 10.5$	8	$(10 + 10.5) \div 2 = 10.25$	$8 \times 10.25 = 82$
$10.5 \leq x < 11$	5	$(10.5 + 11) \div 2 = 10.75$	$5 \times 10.75 = 53.75$
Total	30		$26.25 + 18.5 + 117 + 82 + 53.75 = 297.5$

So an estimate of the mean length is 297.5 ÷ 30 = 9.9166...
= 9.9 cm (to 1 d.p.)
[4 marks available — 1 mark for the correct midpoints, 1 mark for using these to find frequency × mid-interval value, 1 mark for dividing 297.5 by 30, 1 mark for the correct final answer]

Page 100: Frequency Polygons

1

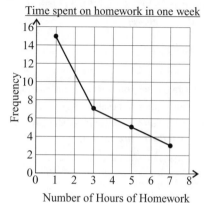

Time spent on homework in one week

Number of Hours of Homework

[2 marks available — 2 marks if all 4 points are plotted correctly and joined up, otherwise 1 mark if either the points are correct but not joined up, or if only 2 or 3 points are correct, or if the points have been plotted at the upper or lower class boundaries and joined up]

2 a) E.g. There was between 4 and 6 mm of rainfall more often in Holcombury than in Ramsbrooke.
[1 mark for any correct comparison]
There are quite a few other comparisons you could make here — for example, you could look at the total rainfall over the 45 days.

b) $(3 \times 1) + (5 \times 3) + (6 \times 5) + (13 \times 7) + (11 \times 9) + (6 \times 11) + (1 \times 13) = 3 + 15 + 30 + 91 + 99 + 66 + 13 = 317$
$317 \div 45 = 7.0444.... = 7.0$ mm (to 1 d.p.)
[3 marks available — 1 mark for multiplying the frequencies by the midpoints, 1 mark for dividing by 45, 1 mark for the correct final answer]

Pages 101-102: Probability Basics

1 a) Certain *[1 mark]*
b) Even *[1 mark]*
c) Unlikely *[1 mark]*

2 a)

```
0               0.5                    1
                 ↑
```

[1 mark]

b)

```
0               0.5                    1
↑
```

[1 mark]

c) $\frac{2}{6} = \frac{1}{3}$
[2 marks available — 1 mark for showing there are 2 chances out of 6, 1 mark for the correct simplified fraction]

3 a) Blue *[1 mark]*
b) $\frac{3}{8}$ *[1 mark]*

4 a) Number of red counters = 10 − 4 = 6 *[1 mark]*
Probability of getting a red counter = $\frac{6}{10} = \frac{3}{5}$ *[1 mark]*
[2 marks available in total — as above]
If the question doesn't tell you how to give your answer, a correct decimal would gain full marks too.

b) There are no green counters, so the probability of getting a green = 0 *[1 mark]*

Answers

5 Total number of people in the team = 6 + 9 + 4 + 1 = 20 *[1 mark]*
   So the probability that person's favourite position is midfield
   = $\frac{9}{20}$ *[1 mark]*
   [2 marks available in total — as above]

6 0.4 + x + 2x = 1 *[1 mark]*
   3x = 1 – 0.4 = 0.6
   x = 0.6 ÷ 3 = 0.2 *[1 mark]*
   P(stripy sock) = 2x, so P(stripy sock) = 2 × 0.2 = 0.4 *[1 mark]*
   [3 marks available in total — as above]

Page 103: More Probability

1 (hockey, netball), (hockey, choir), (hockey, orienteering),
   (orchestra, netball), (orchestra, choir), (orchestra, orienteering),
   (drama, netball), (drama, choir), (drama, orienteering)
   [2 marks available — 2 marks if all 9 possible outcomes are correct, otherwise 1 mark if at least 5 are correct]

2 a)
   Cards

		2	4	6	8	10
	1	3	5	7	9	11
	2	4	6	8	10	12
Dice	**3**	5	7	9	11	13
	4	6	8	10	12	14
	5	7	9	11	13	15
	6	8	10	12	14	16

   [2 marks available — 2 marks if all entries are correct, otherwise 1 mark if at least 4 entries are correct]

   b) 3 ways of scoring exactly 9
   Total number of possible outcomes = 30
   Probability of scoring exactly 9 = $\frac{3}{30}$ *[1 mark]*
   = $\frac{1}{10}$ *[1 mark]*

   [2 marks available in total — as above]

Page 104: Expected Frequency

1 200 × 0.64 = 128 times
   [2 marks available — 1 mark for a correct method, 1 mark for the correct final answer]

2 400 × 0.35 = 140
   [2 marks available — 1 mark for a correct method, 1 mark for the correct final answer]

3 P(lands on 5) = 1 – P(lands on 1, 2, 3 or 4) *[1 mark]*
   P(lands on 5) = 1 – (0.3 + 0.15 + 0.2 + 0.25) = 0.1 *[1 mark]*
   Estimate of number of times spinner lands on 5 = 100 × 0.1 *[1 mark]*
   = 10 times *[1 mark]*

   [4 marks available in total — as above]

Page 105: Relative Frequency

1 a) 50 × 0.12 = 6
       [2 marks available — 1 mark for a correct method, 1 mark for the correct final answer]

   b) 1 and 3 have a much higher relative frequency than the other numbers, so the dice is probably not fair.
       [2 marks available — 1 mark for 'probably not fair' or 'not fair' or 'may not be fair' or similar, 1 mark for an explanation that includes numbers or refers to relative frequency]

   c) She should not expect the same results as there are a large number of possible outcomes all with similar probabilities.
       [1 mark for a correct explanation of why she shouldn't expect the same result]

2 a)

Number on counter	1	2	3	4	5
Frequency	23	25	22	21	9
Relative frequency	0.23	0.25	0.22	0.21	0.09

   [2 marks available — 2 marks for all correct answers, otherwise 1 mark for any frequency ÷ 100]

   b) E.g. No, because the relative frequency for selecting a counter numbered 5 is too low — they should each be around 0.2 if the number of counters is equal.
       [1 mark for saying that he's wrong (or probably wrong) because the relative frequency for 5 is too low]
       It's okay to say that he's probably wrong, because there is a (very) small possibility that he could have got these results even with the same number of each counter.

   ### How to get answers for the Practice Papers

   You can print out worked solutions to Practice Papers 1 & 2 by accessing your free Online Edition of this book (which also includes step-by-step video solutions).

   There's more info about how to get your Online Edition at the front of this book.